DAVID COI

CHARLES DICKENS

Simplified by Michael West

Illustrated by Charles Mosley

1800 word vocabulary

LONGMAN

LONGMAN GROUP LIMITED
London

*Associated companies, branches and representatives
throughout the world*

First published in this series 1940
New edition (reset and re-illustrated) 1964
*New impressions *1964; *1965; *1966 (twice);*
**1967; *1968; *1969; *1970;*
**1971; *1972; *1973; *1974;*
**1975; *1976;*
**1977*

ISBN 0 582 53501 8

This book is written within the 1,800 word vocabulary
of New Method Reader 5 Alternative Edition. All extra
words are explained either in a footnote or in a picture
where they first appear.

*Printed in Hong Kong by
Yu Luen Offset Printing Factory Ltd*

CONTENTS

PART ONE. HOME

PART TWO SCHOOL

PART THREE YOUTH

PART FOUR THE WORLD

page

PART FIVE MARRIAGE

PART SIX SETTLEMENT

THE pronunciation given is the system used in The International Phonetic Alphabet.

BLUNDERSTONE	ˈblʌndəstoun
CANTERBURY	ˈkæntəbəri
CHARLES DICKENS	ˈtʃaalz ˈdikinz
CHATHAM	ˈtʃætəm
CHILLIP	ˈtʃilip
CLARA	ˈkleara
CREAKLE	ˈkriikl
DAVID COPPERFIELD	ˈdeivid ˈkɔpəfiild
DARTLE	ˈdaatl
DAVY	ˈdeivi
DORA	ˈdɔɔrə
DOVER	ˈdouvə
EALING	ˈiiliŋ
GRAPER	ˈgreipə
GUMMIDGE	ˈgʌmidʒ
HOLBORN	ˈhoubən
JORKINS	ˈdʒɔɔkinz
JULIA MILLS	ˈdʒiuliə milz
KIDGERBURY	ˈkidʒəbəri
LITTIMER	ˈlitimə
MICAWBER	miˈkɔɔbə
MOWCHER	ˈmautʃə
MURDSTONE	ˈməədstoun
OXFORD	ˈɔksfəd
PEGGOTTY	ˈpegəti
ROCHESTER	ˈrɔtʃistə
QUINION	ˈkwiniən
SALEM HOUSE	ˈseilem-
SPENLOW	ˈspenlou
STEERFORTH	ˈstiiəfɔɔθ
TRADDLES	ˈtrædlz
URIAH HEEP	iuˈraiə hiip
WATERBROOK	ˈwɔɔtəbruk
WICKFIELD	ˈwikfiild
WILKINS (MICAWBER)	ˈwilkinz
YARMOUTH	ˈiaaməθ

PART ONE

HOME

One

HOW I WAS BORN

My name is David Copperfield, and I am writing the story of my life.

I was born at Blunderstone. My father died before I was born.

One evening my mother was sitting by the fire feeling very sad about herself and the poor fatherless baby.

Then she looked up and saw Miss Betsy outside the garden fence. Miss Betsy walked calmly up to the door; then, instead of ringing the bell, she pressed her nose to the window and looked in.

Miss Betsy was my father's aunt;[1] so she was my great-aunt. Her real name was Miss Trotwood. Miss Betsy Trotwood lived with one servant in a cottage near the sea. She was married once, but her husband was a bad man, so she paid him to go away.

She had always been fond of my father, but she was very angry with him when he married my mother; she said that my mother was a "silly plaything." So my father and Miss Betsy quarrelled, and never met again.

[1] Aunt = mother's or father's sister.

My mother saw Miss Trotwood at the window; so she ran and opened the door.

"You are Mrs. David Copperfield, aren't you?"

"Yes,—please come in," said my mother.

Miss Betsy walked in, and they both sat down.

My mother suddenly began to cry.

"Oh! Oh!" said Miss Betsy, "don't do that!"

But my mother went on crying. Then Miss Betsy took my mother's face in her hands: "Why," she cried, "you are only a baby yourself.—Have some tea. What's the name of your girl?"

"I don't know if the baby will be a girl," said my mother.

"I mean your servant-girl."

"My servant is called Peggotty."

Miss Betsy called Peggotty and made her bring some tea.

"Speaking of the baby," said Miss Trotwood, "I say that it will be a girl; it *must* be a girl; and I ask you to name the girl Betsy Trotwood Copperfield. I shall be her friend.—Do you know anything about cooking and keeping accounts and taking care of a house?"

"Not much," said my mother. "I wish I knew more."

And she started to cry again.

"Don't do that! You will make yourself ill and that will be bad for the baby."

Peggotty came in with the tea. She saw how ill my mother was, and called the doctor.

Mr. Chillip was the name of the doctor. He arrived and went upstairs to my mother.

Hours passed. Then Mr. Chillip came downstairs.

Miss Trotwood

"Well, doctor; how is she?" said Miss Trotwood.

"Mrs. Copperfield is quite comfortable," said the doctor.

"I mean the baby. How is she?"

"It is a boy," said Mr. Chillip.

My aunt did not say a word. She walked straight out of the house and never came back.

And that is how I, David Copperfield, was born.

Two

I BEGIN TO NOTICE THINGS

The earliest memories that I have are my mother with her pretty hair and youthful shape, and Peggotty with no shape at all and very dark eyes and red cheeks like apples. I remember the kitchen and the hens in the yard. The hens seemed very big to me then. I remember the sitting-room where my mother and I and Peggotty sat in the evening. And I remember the outside of our house with the little bedroom windows standing open. And, of course, I remember the garden with a high fence round it. There were fruit trees in the garden. I remember my mother gathering fruit in a basket.

My mother and I were both a little afraid of Peggotty.

Peggotty and I were sitting one night by the fire in the sitting-room. I had been reading to her. I was very tired,—so tired that I could hardly keep my eyes open. I watched her needle passing quickly in and out of the cloth. Then I looked up at her face which I thought beautiful.

"Peggotty," I said suddenly, "were you ever married?"

"Why! David, whatever made you think of marriage?" she said so quickly that it quite woke me up.

"Were you ever married?" I said. "You are a very beautiful woman, aren't you?"

"Me beautiful?—No, dear!"

There was a short silence. Peggotty's needle moved again.

"Peggotty," I said again, "if you marry a person, and the person dies, then you may marry another person, mayn't you, Peggotty?"

"You may if you wish to," said Peggotty; "but I don't say that you should. People have different opinions."

"What is your opinion, Peggotty?" said I.

Peggotty did not answer at once. Then she said, "My opinion is that you should go on reading." Her voice seemed strange. I looked at her.

"You aren't angry with me, Peggotty?" I said.

She kissed the top of my head. "No, dear; but let me hear some more about—those things that you were reading about."

I read on.

Then the door bell rang. We went to the door to open it. There was my mother looking very pretty, and there was a gentleman with her. I had seen this gentleman before; it was the same gentleman who had walked home with her from church last Sunday. His name was Mr. Murdstone.

My mother bent down and kissed me.

"Ah," said the gentleman, "that is a very fortunate young man." He put his hand on my head. I put up my hand and took it away.

"Dear boy!" said the gentleman. "I am not surprised that he loves you!" He bent down and kissed my mother's hand. I was surprised and angry.

"Good night, my dear boy," said the gentleman.

"Good night," said I, but I would not shake hands with him. He turned to go; and, as he did so, he looked at me. He did not look nice. I did not like that gentleman.

We went into the sitting-room.

"I hope you have had a nice evening, Mrs. Copperfield," said Peggotty, standing up very straight in the middle of the room.

"Thank you," said my mother, "I have had a very nice evening."

"It is pleasant to see a stranger sometimes," said Peggotty.

"Yes," said my mother.

I sat in a chair and fell asleep. When I woke up I found Peggotty and my mother talking, and there were tears in their eyes.

"Mr. Copperfield would not have liked such a man," Peggotty was saying.

"Oh!" cried my mother, "you'll make me mad! How dare you speak to me so unkindly! You know that I have no friends to turn to."

"That is a very good reason for speaking. You must not do it! No!" said Peggotty.

"If people like me, what can I do? I can't drive

him away. I can't make myself ugly," said my mother. She came to me. "Dear David, she is saying that I don't love you,—my own little David."

"I did not say that," cried Peggotty.

"You did! You did!—Am I a bad mother, David? Am I cruel and unkind? I do love you, don't I, David?"

We began to cry together. I went to bed feeling very sad, and I fell asleep still crying.

Next Sunday the gentleman walked back from church with my mother. He came in to look at our flowers and asked if he might have one. He came again and again. I became used to seeing the gentleman; but I did not like him.

One morning I was with my mother in the front garden when Mr. Murdstone came along on a horse. He said that he was going to see some friends who were in a sailing-boat at Lowestoft. I was sent upstairs to Peggotty. Peggotty saw my mother and Mr. Murdstone walking up and down in the road. She looked very angry. She brushed my hair very hard and hurt me.

Perhaps it was the next day, or perhaps it was a little later when Peggotty asked me to go with her to visit her brother.

My mother was out. Peggotty and I were sitting in front of the fire. She looked at me several times and opened her mouth as if she were going to speak. Then she shut her mouth without speaking.

"Master Davy," she said at last, "would you like to go along with me and stay for two weeks with my brother at Yarmouth?"

"Is your brother a nice man, Peggotty?" I asked.

"Oh, yes," said Peggotty. "There is the sea at Yarmouth, and boats and ships and fishermen and sand, and there is a boy called Ham for you to play with."

"What will Mother say?" I asked.

"Oh, she will let us go. I will ask her as soon as she comes home. She is going to stay with Mrs. Graper, so we shall not be leaving her alone."

So it was all arranged. The days soon came for our going. We were to go in the carrier's cart.[1]

I remember now how eager I was to leave my happy home.—I did not know what I was leaving for ever.

I remember how my mother stood kissing me at the gate. I cried at the thought of leaving my home. My mother cried too. When the cart began to move my mother ran out of the gate and called to the driver to stop so that she might kiss me once more.

I looked back and saw her standing in the road. I saw Mr. Murdstone go up to her. He seemed angry with her for crying because I was going away.

[1] Carrier's cart = a cart which carries things and people from one place to another.

Three

A VISIT TO MR. PEGGOTTY

The carrier's horse was the laziest horse in the world. It went slowly along with its head down as if it liked to keep people waiting for their things. We went down many little lanes, leaving a box at one house, a bed at another. Peggotty had a basket of food on her knee. We ate a great deal, and we slept a great deal, but it was such a long journey that I was quite tired, and very glad when we saw Yarmouth.

The country at Yarmouth was quite flat; the sea came in among the houses of the town; it was not easy to tell where the town ended and the sea began.

The Carrier's Horse

We came into a street which smelled of fish, and stopped at an inn.

"Here's Ham!" cried Peggotty; "how big he has grown!"

He was a big fellow, six feet high, but his face was like a boy's face and he had light curly hair. He was waiting for us outside the inn. He carried me on his back and my box under his arm. Peggotty carried another box. We turned down lanes covered with sand. We passed boat-builders' houses and rope-makers' houses, and all sorts of places where the different parts of a ship are made. At last we came to an open sandy place.

"There is our house, David," said Ham.

I looked in all directions, but could not see any house anywhere. There was a large black boat not far off with an iron pipe fixed in the top of it, and smoke was coming out of the pipe; but I could not see any other sort of house anywhere.

"Is that it?—that thing that looks like a boat?" I asked.

"Yes, that's it," said Ham.

I was delighted. There was a door cut in the side of the boat and it had little windows in the sides. The top was covered with a roof. What pleased me was that this was a real boat which had been out on the sea. It was never meant to be used as a house on the land. It was such fun to live in a boat on dry land!

We went into the house; it was very clean inside.

There was a table and a clock, and pictures on the wall. There were chairs and boxes used as chairs.

Mr. Peggotty

Then Peggotty opened a little door and showed me my bedroom. It was a very nice little bedroom in the back part of the boat. The walls were white. There was a looking-glass with shells round it. I noticed the very strong smell of fish in the house. Peggotty said that her brother's work was catching shell-fish.

We were welcomed to the house by a very polite woman called Mrs. Gummidge, and there was a beautiful little girl called Emily, who looked at me and then ran away and hid.

We had fish for dinner.

Later a dark hairy[1] man came. He kissed Peggotty (who was his sister). He was Mr. Peggotty.

"I'm glad to see you, sir," said Mr. Peggotty. "We are proud to have you here. I hope you will be happy with her"—he nodded towards Mrs. Gummidge—"and Ham and Little Emily." Then he went off and washed and when he came back his face was very red. I thought that his face was like a shell-fish, which turns red when you put it into the water.

We sat by the fire in the evening, and I learned that Ham was not the son of Mr. Peggotty but of his brother who was drowned at sea. Little Emily was daughter of Mr. Peggotty's brother-in-law, who was also dead. Mr. Gummidge was the friend who worked with Mr. Peggotty in his boat, but he was drowned a long time ago. Then Mr. Peggotty took care of his wife, Mrs. Gummidge, and let her live in his house.

When I went to bed I heard the noise of the wind and the sea and I dreamed that our boat was at sea and that Mr. Peggotty was the captain.

[1] Hairy = having much hair on his face.

Little Emily

Next morning I walked along by the sea with Emily.

"I suppose you love the sea?" I said.

"Oh, no!" she answered. "I'm afraid of it. I have seen it break a boat to pieces, and it is so cruel to our men."

We walked on and came to a *jetty* where the ships

came to the shore. Little Emily walked out to the end of the jetty; she seemed to be walking very near the edge.

"You said that you were afraid of the sea," I said; "but you don't seem to be afraid."

"I'm afraid when there is a storm," she said, "but I'm not afraid of it when it is calm, as it is now." She ran along a board which stood out over the water, so that I felt afraid. Then she came running back. I laughed at my fears, but there have been times in my later life when I have thought that it would have been better if she had fallen into the sea then.

I loved Little Emily. She was only a baby and I was only a little boy, but there is something very beautiful in the pure and simple love of little children. We used to walk about the sands at Yarmouth for hours and hours. Mrs Gummidge and Peggotty whispered about us. "Aren't they beautiful together?" and Mr. Peggotty smiled at us from behind his pipe.

I found that Mrs. Gummidge was not always of a happy nature. Mr. Peggotty went out one evening with some friends. Mrs. Gummidge had been in low spirits all day.

"I am all alone," she said, "and everything goes wrong with me."

She kept complaining about the cold:

"It is very cold to-day; everyone feels it," said Peggotty.

"I feel it more than other people do," said Mrs. Gummidge.

At dinner the fishes were small and full of bones, and they had been burnt in the cooking. We were all rather sad, but Mrs. Gummidge said, "I feel it more than you do,"—and she wept.

When Mr. Peggotty came home at nine o'clock, Mrs. Gummidge was weeping in a corner.

"What's the matter?" he asked. "Why are you crying? Be cheerful!"

"You've been out. I am sorry that I should drive you out," said Mrs. Gummidge.

"Drive me out!" said Mr. Peggotty with a laugh. "I didn't need driving. I wanted to go out."

"I'm all alone, and nobody likes me.—I feel things more than other people do. I am not what I could wish to be. I make this house uncomfortable."—She went away to bed.

"She has been thinking of the Old One."

I asked Peggotty who the Old One was. She told me that this meant her husband who had died.

The two weeks went by. It was the end of my visit. I was very sad at leaving Little Emily. We walked arm-in-arm to the place where the carrier's cart started, and as the cart moved away I felt an emptiness in my heart; but I was glad to be on my way to my mother. I said so. But Peggotty did not seem so happy. She seemed very sad.

We reached the house at last. I remember the cold grey afternoon and the dark rain clouds.

The door opened and I ran towards it full of joy. But there was a strange servant at the door.

"Why! Peggotty!" I said; "hasn't she come home?"

"Yes, yes, David," said Peggotty. "She's come home——. Wait; I will tell you something."

"What is the matter?" I asked anxiously. "Why hasn't Mother come to the gate? Is she dead? No! No! She isn't dead?"

"No!" said Peggotty. "I ought to have told you before. You have got a new father."

My face was white.

"Come and see him," she said.

We went into the sitting-room, and she left me there.

On one side of the fire sat my mother, and on the other side sat Mr. Murdstone.

Four

I GET INTO TROUBLE

My bedroom had been changed to another room. I lay on my bed, pulled the sheet over my head, and cried until I fell asleep.

I was awakened by someone saying, "Here he is," and pulling away the sheet. My mother and Peggotty had come to look for me.

"David," said my mother. "What is the matter?"

"Nothing," I said, and turned over.

"You have done this," said my mother, turning to Peggotty. "You have been speaking against me. Oh, David, you bad boy! Peggotty, you bad woman! Oh, what a lot of troubles there are in the world when I've just been married and ought to be so happy."

Then I felt the touch of a hand which was neither hers not Peggotty's. It was Mr. Murdstone.

Mr. Murdstone and his sister

"What's this?" he said. "Clara, my dear, have you forgotten what I told you? You must be firm."

"I am so sorry, Edward," said my mother. "But it is so hard to be firm."

He whispered in her ear. I knew that he could do with her anything that he wished.

"Go downstairs, my dear," he said. "David and I will understand each other."

My mother and Peggotty went out.

"David," said Mr. Murdstone, "do you know how I make a horse or a dog obey me?"

"I don't know."

"I beat him.—I say to myself, 'I will conquer that animal if I have to beat out every drop of blood in his body.' Do you understand me?—Yes, I see that you understand. Wash your face and come downstairs with me."

"Clara, my dear," he said, when we came into the sitting-room, "you will not be made uncomfortable by this child any more."

After dinner a carriage came to the door. Miss Murdstone had arrived. She was dark, like her brother. She had brought two black boxes with iron bands on them. She kept her money in a little bag made of iron. She was an iron woman.

She looked at me. "I don't like most boys." She shook hands with me.

"He has got no manners," said Miss Murdstone.

We met again next morning at the breakfast-table.

"Now, Clara," she said, "I have come to help you. You are far too pretty and thoughtless to do anything which I can do for you. If you will give me your keys,

I will take care of all the house-matters in future."

My mother began to cry.

"Clara! " said Mr. Murdstone. "I am surprised! "

"You talk about firmness," said my mother, "but you would not like so much of it yourself. It is very hard that in my own house——"

"*My* own house," said Mr. Murdstone. "Did you say 'my'? "

"I mean *our* house," said my mother, looking very frightened. "It's very hard not to be able to manage anything or do anything in our own house. I'm sure I managed very well before we were married. Ask Peggotty."

"Edward," said Miss Murdstone, "I shall go away to-morrow! "

"Jane Murdstone," said her brother; "be silent! "

"Clara! " he said. "I had hoped, when I married you, to be able to give you some of that firmness which you need. When my sister, Jane Murdstone, was kind enough to come and help me in this, I expected you to thank her. When you speak as you do, I am pained. My feelings are changed."

"Oh, don't say that," cried my mother. "I do thank her. Oh, do let us be friends. I can't live where people are unkind to me."

"David," said Mr. Murdstone, "this is not a fit scene for a boy. Leave the room! "

I was crying so much that I could hardly find the door. After that Miss Murdstone took complete charge of the house. If my mother said anything or gave any opinion Miss Murdstone would begin to open her bag as if to give back the keys; then my mother became frightened and silent.

I had lessons with my mother. My mother was supposed to be teaching me, but Mr. Murdstone and his sister were always present; and they used my lessons as a chance for teaching my mother firmness. In the old days, before my mother married Mr. Murdstone, I used to enjoy my lessons and I learnt easily. But these solemn lessons with the Murdstones were things of fear and pain. They were a daily trial and sorrow—to my mother as well as to me.

I came into the room and gave the book to my mother, and started to say my lesson. I started speaking quickly while it was fresh in my mind; then I missed a word. Mr. Murdstone looked up, and that frightened me so much that I missed another word. Miss Murdstone looked up: I missed six or seven words. My mother wanted to help me, but she dared not do so.

" Oh, David," she said.

" Now, Clara," said Mr. Murdstone, " be firm with the boy. Don't say ' Oh, David.' Does he know his lesson? "

" He does *not* know it," said Miss Murdstone.

" I'm really afraid he does not," said my mother.

" Then give him back the book and *make* him know it," said Miss Murdstone.

"Yes," said my mother; "that is what I meant to do. Now, David, try again. Don't be foolish."

I tried again, and failed at the same place. Mr. Murdstone made an impatient movement; Miss Murdstone did the same. My mother tried to help me by moving her lips.

" Clara! " said Miss Murdstone.

Mr. Murdstone came out of his chair. He took the

book, hit me on the head and threw me out of the room.

Such were my lessons day after day. Even when I did well I was given more work to do, because the Murdstones did not wish me to sit doing nothing. I became silent, unhappy. My only happiness was a set of books which belonged to my father. I found them in a room near my own. I had *Robinson Crusoe* and *The Vicar of Wakefield* and a book of travels, and many other books. These books were a way of escaping from the unhappiness of my life.

Five

I AM BEATEN

One morning I went into the sitting-room with my book. I saw my mother looking anxious; Miss Murdstone was looking firm, and Mr. Murdstone had a stick in his hand.

"I tell you, Clara," said Mr. Murdstone, "that I have often been beaten myself."

"Yes, of course," said Miss Murdstone.

"Yes, my dear Jane," said my mother; "but do you think that it did Edward good?"

"Do you think that it did Edward harm?" asked Miss Murdstone.

Mr. Murdstone looked at me, still holding the stick in his hand. "Now, David," he said, "you must be more careful than usual"; and he held up the stick.

Of course I was worse than usual. I began badly and

went on worse. I could not remember anything. At last my mother began to cry.

"Clara!" said Miss Murdstone.

"I am not feeling well to-day," said my mother.

"Clara, you are not yet firm enough to bear the trouble which this boy has given you to-day. David, you and I will go upstairs."

As he led me out of the door, my mother ran towards me. Miss Murdstone said, "Clara! are you a perfect fool?" I heard my mother crying as we went upstairs.

"Oh, Mr. Murdstone, sir!" I cried, "please don't beat me. I have tried to learn, but I can't learn when you and Miss Murdstone are near."

He took my head under his arm. Then I bit his hand. Then he beat me as if he would beat me to death. We made a terrible noise. He was beating; I was crying out; and, above the noise of the beating, I heard them running upstairs, and I heard my mother and Peggotty crying. Then he was gone. The door was locked. And I was lying on the floor.

After a time I became quiet. I listened. There was not a sound in the house. I looked at my face in the glass—so red and swollen that it frightened me. I felt terribly[1] bad—as if I had done some terribly bad thing. What would happen to me? Would I be sent to prison?

Then the door opened; Miss Murdstone came in with some bread and milk. She put them down on the table; then she looked at me firmly, went out, and locked the door again.

---

[1] Terribly = very, fearfully.

Six

I AM SENT TO SCHOOL

I woke next morning. I felt quite bright and happy; and then the terrible memory came back to me. I wondered whether I should be hanged, or what would be done to me.

I stayed there for five days. Those days are like years in my memory. I listened to all the sounds of the house—the ringing of bells, footsteps on the stairs, voices in the street outside.

On the last day I heard my name spoken in a whisper. I went to the door:

"Is that you, Peggotty dear?"

"Yes, David. Be very quiet or She will hear us."

(*She* meant Miss Murdstone.)

"How is Mother, dear Peggotty? Is she very angry with me?"

I could hear Peggotty crying. "No. Not very angry," said Peggotty.

"What are they going to do with me, Peggotty dear? Do you know?"

"School. Near London," was Peggotty's answer.

"When, Peggotty?"

"To-morrow."

Then Peggotty put her mouth close to the keyhole. "David dear," she said, "I have not seen you much lately, but that is not because I don't love you. I love you just as much as ever. But I thought it better not to see you—better for you and for your mother. I thought that they would be angry. The day may come

There were tears in my mother's eyes

when she will be glad to lay her head on Peggotty's arm again. I'll write to you, my dear." She was crying.

"Thank you, dear Peggotty," I said. "And will you write and tell Mr. Peggotty and Little Emily that I'm not so bad as they might think, and that I send my love to all of them, especially to Little Emily? Will you please do that?"

She promised.

In the morning Miss Murdstone came and told me that I was going to school. I found my mother at the breakfast-table. Her eyes were red with crying.

"Oh, David," she said, "do try to be a good boy."

They had made her believe that I was a bad boy. I tried to eat, but my tears fell upon my bread-and-butter.

The carrier's cart came up to the gate. My box was taken down and put on it. Peggotty did not appear.

"Clara!" said Miss Murdstone; "be firm!"

"Yes, dear Jane," said my mother. "Good-bye, Davy. You are going for your own good. Good-bye, my child. You will come home for the holidays and be a better boy."

There were tears in my mother's eyes.

"Clara!" said Miss Murdstone again.

"Yes, dear Jane," said my mother. "God bless you, David."

Miss Murdstone took me out to the cart. I got in. The lazy horse moved away.

PART TWO

SCHOOL

Seven

ON THE WAY TO SCHOOL

I cried so much that my handkerchief was quite wet. Then the carrier stopped. I wondered why he had stopped. Peggotty climbed into the cart. She kissed me; then she brought out some paper-bags full of cake which she put into my pockets and a little bag of money, which she put into my hand. Then she got down from the cart and ran away.

The cart moved on.

After a time I stopped crying. The carrier put my handkerchief on the back of the horse to dry. I looked in the little bag of money; there were three bright shillings in it, and a paper " *For David, with my love.*"

I asked the carrier, " Are we going all the way there? "

" All the way *where?* " asked the carrier.

" There," I said.

" Where is ' there '? " asked the carrier.

" London," I asked.

" Why that horse would be dead before he got half that distance. I'm only going to Yarmouth, and the *coach* will take you to London." This was a long speech for Mr. Barkis. (Barkis was the name of the carrier.)

I offered him a cake. He put it in his big mouth and swallowed it whole.

"Did she make that?" he said.

"Do you mean Peggotty, sir?—Yes, she did. She does all the cooking."

Mr. Barkis sat looking at the horse's ears, and thinking for a long time.

Then he said, "No husband?"

"No, sir. She is not married."

He sat looking at the horse's ears.

"So she does all the cooking?"

"Yes," I answered.

"Perhaps you will be writing to her?" he said.

"Yes," I answered.

"Well," he answered, slowly turning his eyes towards me, "if you are writing to her, say that Barkis is willing."[1]

"'Barkis is willing.'—Is that all the message?" said I, not understanding.

"Yes," he said slowly.

"But you will be passing my home to-morrow, Mr. Barkis. Could you not give your own message better?"

"'Barkis is willing.' That's the message," he said.

When we reached Yarmouth, the lady in charge of the inn said that dinner had been ordered for me. She led me into a very large room. The waiter brought me my dinner.

"That looks a very big dinner for a little boy," he said. "Shall I help you with it? Let us see who can eat most."

The waiter ate most. He ate nearly all the dinner.

[1] This is a peculiar way of saying that he wishes to marry her.

I asked him for some paper and I wrote a letter to Peggotty:

MY DEAR PEGGOTTY,

I have come here safe. Barkis is willing. Give my love to Mother.

Yours with much love,

DAVID.

Note.—He says that he specially wants you to know—*Barkis is willing.*

"Are you going to school?" asked the waiter.

"Yes," I said.

"Where is the school?"

I said, "Near London. That is all I know."

"Oh! I am sorry for that."

"Why?" I asked.

"That's the school where they broke two bones in a boy's side."

This did not make me feel very happy.

The coach came to the door.

The lady of the inn came and looked at me, and led me to the coach.

"Did you eat all that dinner without being helped? —George!" she said to the servant, "take care of that child or he will burst."

I got into the coach. It drove away.—At last I reached London in the morning. There one of the masters of the school was waiting for me. His name was Mr. Mell. I said that I had had no breakfast.

"We will buy some food," said Mr. Mell. "I have to visit an old lady; you may eat it at her house."

We walked a short distance and came to some *almshouses*. (These are small houses built by some rich man for very poor people to live in.) Mr. Mell went into one of these houses.

"My Charley!" said the woman. She was Mr. Mell's mother.

We sat down and ate breakfast. Afterwards the old woman said, "Have you got your whistle, Charley?"

He took out a whistle and began to play a very sad tune. I have never heard anyone play worse.

We went back and got into another coach. It drove away and we came at last to Blackheath.

We walked a short distance and came to a high brick wall. Over a door in this wall there was a board with SALEM HOUSE written upon it.

The door was opened by a man with a wooden leg.

"The new boy," said the master.

Salem House was a square, sad-looking brick building. I was led into a schoolroom—the saddest and emptiest place I have ever seen. It was a long room with three long lines of desks in it. Bits of paper lay on the floor. The walls were covered with ink as if a rain of ink had come through the roof, and there was a strange unpleasant smell in the air. For some days I was alone in the place with Mr. Mell. The boys had not come back yet from the holidays; and Mr. Creakle, the headmaster, was away at the sea. I had my meals with Mr. Mell in a big empty hall. I sat in a class-room, alone with Mr. Mell. He wrote, and when he had finished writing he pulled out his whistle and played sad tunes on it. I read, or listened to the whistle, and cried myself to sleep when I went to bed at night in a great big room with many empty beds in it.

Eight

I MEET MANY NEW PEOPLE

The man with a wooden leg began to clean up the school building. I was told that Mr. Creakle would be home that evening. Just before I went to bed I was called by the man with a wooden leg to go to the headmaster.

Mr. Creakle was a fat man. He sat in an armchair. Mrs. Creakle and Miss Creakle were also in the room.

"So!" he said, "this is the young gentleman who bites.—I have been told by Mr. Murdstone that you bite. I know Mr. Murdstone; he is a man of strong character. I also am a man of strong character. When I say that I *will* have a thing done, I will have it done."

I was very frightened.

Next day Mr. Sharp, the other master, came back. The first boy who returned was Tommy Traddles. Later came the other boys, and J. Steerforth. I was taken to J. Steerforth as if he was a judge. He sat in a shed in the playground. He was head boy; he was very clever, and very good-looking.

"How much money have you got?" he asked.

I told him—seven shillings.

"You may give it to me," he said, "and I will take care of it for you." So I did this.

"Perhaps you would like to spend some of it on a feast to be eaten in the bedroom?" he said.

I said, "Yes."

So that night we had a feast in the bedroom. We all sat round and talked in whispers, and I learnt many things about the school—that Mr. Creakle beat the boys very much, that he knew nothing, that he had been a shopkeeper before he started the school, that he never dared to beat J. Steerforth, that Mr. Sharp and Mr. Mell were paid very little, that Mrs. Creakle admired Steerforth very much.

"Good night, young Copperfield," said Steerforth. "I'll take care of you."

"You are very kind," I said. "Thank you."

Nine

MY FIRST TERM AT SALEM HOUSE

School began next day. I remember the deep roar of many voices in the class-room, and the sudden silence as Mr. Creakle came in. Mr. Creakle seemed to take a special pleasure in beating boys and he beat poor Traddles most of all.

Steerforth continued to be my protector. I told him stories at night and he helped me with my lessons. Mr. Mell also helped me; he seemed to like me. It always gave me pain to notice that Steerforth treated Mr. Mell so badly. He seemed to do everything to hurt his feelings and make others do so. This troubled me all the more because I had told Steerforth that Mr. Mell's mother lived in an almshouse and I was always afraid that Steerforth would tell them and make fun of Mr. Mell because of it.

So school went on from day to day. And then there came the day which I shall remember all my life.

It was a Saturday. As it was a wet day we had to pass the afternoon in the schoolroom. Mr. Sharp was out, so Mr. Mell was left in charge.

The boys made more noise than usual. They ran about, laughed, shouted, sang, danced. They stood round Mr. Mell, made faces at him, laughed at his poor clothes, his broken boots, his mother. It was terrible. They were like dogs round some wounded animal. He stayed with his head on his hand, trying to read—pretending to read.

"Silence!" cried Mr. Mell at last, jumping up. "What does this mean? It's impossible to bear it. It is driving me mad. How can you do it to me, boys?" He struck the desk with his book.

Some of the boys stopped, but Steerforth stood at the end of the room whistling.

"Silence, Steerforth!" said Mr. Mell.

"You be silent," said Steerforth.

"Sit down," said Mr. Mell.

"Sit down yourself," said Steerforth.

Some boys laughed. Mr. Mell's face was white.

"I have seen you," said Mr. Mell, "urging on the younger boys to make fun of me. You are a favourite[1] of the headmaster. You use that position as favourite to insult[2] a gentleman."

"To insult a *what*?" said Steerforth. "You are not a gentleman. You are a beggar."

I thought that he was going to strike Mr. Mell, or that Mr. Mell was going to strike him.

Mr. Creakle came into the room.

[1] Favourite = most favoured, most loved child (or person).
[2] Insult = be very rude to.

" What is this? "

" Why did he start talking about favourites? " said Steerforth.

" He used his position as favourite of the head-master to insult me," said Mr. Mell.

" I called him a beggar," said Steerforth, "and he is a beggar, and he is the son of a beggar; his mother lives in an almshouse."

Mr. Mell looked at me. He laid his hand on my shoulder.

" Now, Mr. Mell," said Mr. Creakle, "will you please tell us all that Steerforth is wrong."

" He is right," said Mr. Mell. "What he said is true."

" I think," said Mr. Creakle, "that you mistook this for a school for beggars. You may leave the school."

Mr. Mell stood up.

" Steerforth," he said, "I hope that the time will come when you will be ashamed of what you have done to-day."

He took up his books and his whistle and went out of the room.

" You have insulted him," said Traddles. "You have lost him his work." But most of us thought that Steerforth was wonderful.

One afternoon I was told that there were visitors for me. I went out and saw Mr. Peggotty and Ham.

" How big you have grown! " said Mr. Peggotty.

" How is my mother? " I asked. "And how is Little Emily, and Mrs. Gummidge? "

" All well, all very well," he said. "I've brought you some shell-fish," he said.

Steerforth came into the room. "You must meet my

friends," I said. "These are two Yarmouth boatmen."

"I'm pleased to meet you," said Steerforth.

"May I bring Steerforth to see your house some day?" I asked Peggotty. "It's made out of a boat, Steerforth."

"My house isn't anything to see, but I'll be glad to have you both there," said Mr. Peggotty.

School went on. The days passed, each much the same as the other. Term came to an end. I remember travelling in the coach to Yarmouth.

Ten

THE HOLIDAYS

At Yarmouth I climbed into the carrier's cart.

"You look very well, Mr. Barkis," I said.—"I gave your message."

"Yes," said Mr. Barkis. "But there was no answer. I'm still waiting."

"Have you told her this?" I asked.

"No. You must tell her. Say 'Peggotty, Barkis is waiting for an answer.' Then she will say 'An answer to what?' And you must say, 'Barkis is willing.'"

Then he asked, "What is her other name?"

"Clara," I said. "Clara Peggotty."

He wrote these names on the side of the cart.

The carrier put my box down at the garden gate and left me. I walked along the path towards the house, and I went quickly into the sitting-room. My mother was sitting with a baby in her arms.

I spoke to her. She stood up and cried out and came half across the room to meet me.

"He's your brother," she said. "David, my dear boy, my poor child." Then she kissed me. And then Peggotty came running in.

Mr. and Miss Murdstone were out. So we three had dinner by the fire-side. As we ate, I told Peggotty about Mr. Barkis. She laughed.

"What is the matter?" asked my mother.

"Oh, the silly man wants to marry me."

"That would be a good marriage," said my mother.

"No," said Peggotty. "I wouldn't marry him if he was made of gold.—Tell him," she said, looking at me, "that he has never spoken to me, and if he does, I shall slap[1] his face."

Dinner ended. We sat by the fire.

"Peggotty," said my mother, "are you going to be married?"

"Me? No! No!—Never."

"Don't leave me, Peggotty," said my mother. "Stay with me. It will not be for long."

"Me leave you! Of course not. I shall stay with you till I am an old woman, too old to be of use to anyone."

I told them all about the school.

"I wonder," said Peggotty, "what has happened to David's great-aunt, Miss Betsy Trotwood."

"I suppose she is still in her cottage by the sea. She is not likely to trouble us again."

"Perhaps she might forgive David for being a boy —now that he has got a brother."

[1] Slap = hit with the open hand.

Then my mother began to cry. "Why do you think that David should go away to Miss Trotwood just because I have got a baby brother for him?"

Then they quarrelled and my mother cried; and then they forgave each other and my mother said that Peggotty was her "true friend."

The sound of wheels was heard. Mr. and Miss Murdstone came in. He gave me his hand—the hand which I had bitten. I could see the red mark on it.

I greeted Miss Murdstone.

"How long are the holidays?" she asked.

"A month," I said.

She wrote down the days on a piece of paper and crossed out one day every morning.

They were very unhappy holidays. The Murdstones did not like me. My mother was afraid to be kind to me when they were in the room and she was all the time afraid that I might do or say something which would cause trouble. So I kept myself away. I sat in my bedroom and read; or I sat in the kitchen with Peggotty, and when I was with the Murdstones I remained silent.

Then Mr. Murdstone said that I had a sullen[1] character. "I must try to change that character. You keep away from this room and from us as if we had some dangerous illness."

So I remained sadly in the sitting-room day after day, and hoped for night to come when I could go to bed and be alone.

The holidays went on. At last Miss Murdstone was

[1] Sullen = silent and angry.

able to look up from her paper and say, "Here is the last day."

Barkis came to the gate and my boxes were put on the cart. My mother kissed me, and Miss Murdstone said, "Clara! Be firm," and the cart moved away.

My mother was standing at the gate holding the baby in her arms.

That was the last time I saw my mother alive.

Eleven

1 LOSE MY MOTHER

It was about two months after I came back to Salem House. Mr. Sharp came into the class-room and told me to go to Mr. Creakle. I thought that perhaps some present had come for me from Peggotty.

I found Mr. Creakle sitting at his breakfast. Mrs. Creakle had an open letter in her hand. She made me sit down and came and sat by my side.

"I have something to tell you, my child," she said. "Your mother is very ill."

I began to cry.

"She is dangerously ill."

I knew what she was going to say next.

"She is dead."

I left Salem House on the next afternoon. Mr. Barkis was not in the carrier's cart at Yarmouth, but a little fat man with a red face.

Peggotty met me at the gate and led me into the

house. She was crying. She spoke in a whisper, as if afraid to wake the dead. I went in. Mr. Murdstone was sitting by the fire weeping. Miss Murdstone was busy writing.

A few days later we all stood together by my mother's grave.

Then, afterwards, Peggotty came into my room and sat down by the side of the bed.

"She has not been well for á long time. She wasn't happy. She sang to her baby, very softly. She became more and more frightened, so that a hard word was like a blow. . . . Then one night she said to me: 'Peggotty dear, I think I am dying. I am very tired. If this is sleep, sit by me while I sleep. . . . Put your arm under my neck and turn me to you; your face is far away and I want it to be near.'—And she died like a child that has gone to sleep."

Twelve

PEGGOTTY MARRIES

Soon after my mother was put in her grave, Miss Murdstone told Peggotty that she did not need her any more. Peggotty decided to go and stay with her brother in Yarmouth until she was able to find other work.

"Now I've been thinking," she said, "that perhaps they don't want you here at present and they might let you come with me."

Peggotty and Barkis

Miss Murdstone agreed. I was allowed to go with Peggotty.

Mr. Barkis came and put our boxes in his cart. He was very polite to Peggotty all the time, but he said little. When we came to the end of our journey he called me to one side.

"You know who is willing? Barkis is willing," he said.

As we walked along the street Peggotty asked, "David dear, what would you say if I—got married?"

"To Mr. Barkis? I think it would be a good thing, because you would always have the horse and cart and you could come and see me."

The days passed in Peggotty's house much as they had passed before, but Little Emily and I did not wander on the sand now. She had lessons to do, and work to do in the house. She liked me; she laughed at me; she made fun of me. She was older now—not a baby as before.

Mr. Barkis came every evening and left a present for Peggotty,—fruit, a bird in a cage, a piece of meat, and other strange things. He took Peggotty for walks, and when Peggotty came back, she laughed and laughed.

Barkis took Peggotty and Emily and me for a ride in the cart. He and Peggotty went into a church leaving us alone in the cart. When they came out he said to me:

"What name did I write up in the cart? Clara Peggotty. Well, now it is Clara Barkis."

They had been married in the church.

PART THREE

YOUTH

Thirteen

I GO OUT INTO THE WORLD

Soon after this I had to go home. Barkis drove me back in the cart. Peggotty was with him. They left me at the gate. It was a strange thing to see the cart go on, taking Peggotty away.

And now came the darkest part of my life. Mr. Murdstone hated me. He and his sister never spoke to me. I lived as a stranger in the house. I would gladly have gone to any school, to the hardest school rather than live in this way. Peggotty came to see me every week; and I had my story-books. They were my only friends.

Then one day a man named Quinion came to the house.

Mr. Murdstone called me into the sitting-room.

" This is Mr. Quinion of Murdstone & Co. You will work in Mr. Quinion's office in London. You will live in lodgings."

Soon I was sitting by Mr. Quinion's side in the coach which was taking me to London—a little boy, all alone, going out into the world.

Fourteen

I BEGIN WORK

There were three other boys in the office. I did not like them. I was very unhappy. We worked until twelve on the first day. At twelve o'clock Mr. Quinion called me into his room. I went in and found there a small fat man in a brown coat. His name was Mr. Micawber.

"This," said Mr. Quinion, "is the boy."

"This," said Mr. Micawber, with a curious solemn politeness, "is Master Copperfield? I hope that you are well, Master Copperfield."

I said that I was very well and hoped that he was.

"I am," said Micawber, "thank heaven, very well. I have had a letter from Mr. Murdstone in which he asks me to receive you in my house in a room which is not being used—at present."

"Your lodgings are at Mr. Micawber's house," said Mr. Quinion.

"My address," said Mr. Micawber, "is Windsor House, City Road; in short,[1] I live there.

"I believe that you may not yet know all the streets of this great city and may have difficulty in discovering the house in which I live; in short, you may lose yourself. So I will come and show you the way this evening."

[1] In short = speaking in a few words. Mr. Micawber usually says things in a long and difficult way; then he says them again "in short."

Mr. Micawber put on his hat and marched away

Mr. Micawber put on his hat and marched away. He came back in the evening and led me to his house. There I found Mrs. Micawber with four children.

"I never thought when I was at home with my father and mother," said Mrs. Micawber, "that I should ever have to take a lodger. But Mr. Micawber has difficulties about money. The people to whom he owes money will not give him enough time to pay."

Poor Mrs. Micawber. She was trying to do her best. There was a notice on the door "Mrs. Micawber's School for Young Ladies," but no young ladies ever came there. The only people who came were people coming for money. They shouted at him in the street and shouted up at the windows. At these times Mr. Micawber became very sad and said that he would kill himself, but half an hour later he cleaned his shoes, and went out singing a song, happier than ever. Mrs. Micawber was the same: at six o'clock I saw her lying on the floor weeping, but an hour later I never saw her more cheerful, telling me stories about her father and mother and her home. Mr. Micawber wept at the beginning of the meal, and sang a happy song at the end of it. He came home in the evening crying out that now nothing was left and he would be sent to prison, yet before he went to bed he was working out what it would cost to put new and larger windows in the house;—"in case anything turns up."[1]

They began to sell their things so as to get food.

They dared not carry them out of the house themselves because the men to whom they owed money were watching the place to stop anything being sold.

[1] If, by chance, they got some unexpected good fortune.

I carried out books and pieces of silver in my pockets or under my coat and brought back the money.

At last the end came. Mr. Micawber was taken to prison. I went to visit him there and had dinner with him.

I went back to Mrs. Micawber and comforted her. All the furniture was taken away except a few chairs and a table. We lived among these for some days. Then Mrs. Micawber went to live in the prison, and I went and lived near, and I used to spend the evening in the prison with the Micawbers. At last the Micawbers were set free. They came and stayed for some time in the house where I was. On their last Sunday (before they went away to Plymouth) I went to dinner with them. At the end of dinner Mr. Micawber made a speech.

"My dear young friend," said Mr. Micawber, "I am older than you. I have had more experience of life. Until something turns up (which I am expecting) I have nothing to give you except advice. My advice is: —yearly income[1] £20, yearly expenses £19 19s. 6d., result happiness: yearly expenses[2] £20 0s. 6d., result unhappiness and ruin: the flower is faded, the leaf is dried up, and the sun goes down upon a desert. In short you are ruined, as I am."

In order to make this clear Mr. Micawber sang a song and danced.

Next morning they all went away, and I decided that I would go to the only relation I had, my aunt,

[1] Income = all the money received.
[2] Expenses = money which is spent.

Miss Betsy Trotwood. I packed my box. There was a young man with an empty cart near the corner of the road.

"Will you take this box to the coach?" I said; "—the coach which is going to Dover. How much do you want?"

"Sixpence," he said.

I did not like the young man, but I agreed. I put my box on the cart, then took out my bag of money. Then the young man seized the bag of money from my hand and drove away quickly. I had no money! I had nothing left in the world!—I started to walk to Dover.

I reached Blackheath and slept in a field near Salem House. Next day I reached Rochester, and from there I came to Chatham. I decided to sell my coat so as to get food. I went into a little shop in which there was an ugly old man.

"Oh, my eyes and legs!" said the ugly old man. "What do you want? Oh, my ears and arms! What do you want? Grrrrr!"

"I want to know," I said, "if you will buy a coat. Will you give me two-and-sixpence for it?"

"Oh, my heart and stomach!" said the old man; "no. One shilling and sixpence."

"I agree," I said.

But he did not want to give me the money. I waited a long time, and then at last he paid it me all in half-pennies, one halfpenny at a time.

I walked on and at last came to Dover, and to my aunt's cottage.

My aunt was in the garden.

As soon as I came, she said: "Go away. No boys here!"

"Please, Miss Betsy," I said, "I am David Copperfield. My mother is dead, and I am very unhappy."

I could not say any more. I began to cry.

She went into the house and said to the servant: "Please call Mr. Dick."

Mr. Dick seemed to be rather mad.

"Mr. Dick," said my aunt, "this is David Copperfield."

"Oh, yes, yes!" he said.

"Now don't pretend to be mad, when you are really quite clever," said my aunt. "This is David Copperfield. Tell me, what shall I do with him?"

"Well," said Mr. Dick, looking at me, "wash him."

So I was given a bath.

We had dinner. After dinner I told my aunt all that had happened. My aunt listened.

"Well, I can't understand it," said my aunt. "Why do people go and get married? Your mother got married and then she did it again! And that woman Peggotty, she got married."

She turned to Mr. Dick.

"Now, Mr. Dick," said my aunt, "what shall I do with him now?"

"Oh," said Mr. Dick, "I should put him to bed."

Fifteen

MY AUNT DECIDES

I found my aunt sitting at the breakfast-table.

" I have written to Mr. Murdstone," she said. " And now will you please go upstairs to Mr. Dick."

"Yes," I said.

" He is my relation," said Miss Betsy.

" Is he a little mad? "

" His brother was going to put him in a madhouse, but I let him come and live with me. He is a very kind man and gives very good advice, although he is a little mad. He talks much about King Charles's[1] head and is writing a paper to the judge about his own matters and business, but King Charles always comes into it and he has to start again."

I went upstairs. Mr. Dick showed me a *kite*.[2] The kite was covered all over with writing about King Charles's head.

"This is how I send my ideas out all over the world," he said. " When a kite goes up, my ideas go up."

A few days later Mr. and Miss Murdstone arrived at the cottage. They sat down.

"You are the Mr. Murdstone who married Mrs. Copperfield? "

"Yes," said Mr. Murdstone.

[1] The head of Charles I, King of England, was cut off by the followers of Cromwell in 1649.
[2] A Kite is a toy which is flown in a high wind.

"And this is her son?" said Miss Trotwood.

"Yes," said Mr. Murdstone. "He has run away from his friends and his work. He caused us much trouble."

"Of all boys in the world, this is the worst boy," said Miss Murdstone.

"But," said Mr. Murdstone, "I have come to take him back. Is he ready to go? If he is not, my doors are shut against him. And I understand that your doors are open."

"What does the boy think?" said my aunt. "Does he wish to go back?"

"No, no!" I said. "They never liked me. They were unkind to me. They made my mother unhappy. Please, please don't send me back."

"Mr. Dick," said my aunt, "what shall I do with this child?"

Mr. Dick thought for a long time. Then he said, "I should buy some clothes for him."

Then my aunt looked at Mr. Murdstone.

"I will take the boy," she said. "I don't believe a word of what you have said about him. I can see what happened. Before you were married you told his mother that you would be another father to the child, and when you had married her you began to train her. She was a loving woman, but you were cruel to her. You were cruel to her son. You hate him because the sight of him makes you remember how cruel you were."

Mr. Murdstone stood by the door. His face was white.

"Good-bye to you, sir. Good-bye, Miss Murdstone."

They went out. I kissed my aunt and shook hands with Mr. Dick.

"I shall call you David Trotwood Copperfield," said my aunt.

And so I began a new life under a new name, and all that had happened before seemed very far away.

Sixteen

I MAKE A NEW BEGINNING

Mr. Dick and I soon became very good friends. We often went out together to fly the great kite. Every day of his life he sat and worked hard on the letter to the judge, but he never got any distance in it, because, however hard he tried, King Charles the First always came into it and he had to throw it away and begin again. The kite was made of old letters which he had thrown away. He never looked so peaceful as when he was flying his kite. As it went up higher and higher into the air it seemed to lift his mind out of its madness; and as it came to earth again, and lay there like a dead thing, he seemed to wake up out of a dream. I saw him take up his kite and look about him, as if he was lost,—as if he and the kite had come down to earth together. And I felt sorry for him.

My aunt was very kind to me. She shortened my name from Trotwood to Trot.

"Trot," said my aunt one evening, "I must not

Mr. Wickfield entered the room

forget about your schooling. Would you like to go to a school in Canterbury?"

"Yes," said I, "I would like that very much."

"Good," said my aunt, "would you like to go to-morrow?"

So next day we drove to Canterbury.

"We are going to Mr. Wickfield's house first," said my aunt. "He is a lawyer."[1]

We stopped before a very old house whose windows stood out over the road. Two very white stone steps led up to the door, and the windows were made of strange little squares of glass.

When the carriage stopped in front of the door I saw a white face appear at one of the windows. Then the door was opened by a man called Uriah Heep. He had a white face, red hair cut very short, red-brown eyes, and high shoulders. He was dressed in black. His hand was long and thin; I noticed this as he stood at the horse's head rubbing his cheek.

"Is Mr. Wickfield at home, Uriah Heep?" said my aunt.

"Yes, Mr. Wickfield is at home," said Uriah. "Please walk in." He pointed with a long hand to the sitting-room. There was a picture of a gentleman with grey hair and a beautiful lady with a very peaceful face above the fireplace.

We went into the sitting-room. Mr. Wickfield, the gentleman of the picture, entered the room. "Well, Miss Trotwood," he said, "what brings you here?" He looked some years older than his picture.

[1] Lawyer = man who gives advice on matters of law.

"This is David Trotwood Copperfield. I am his great-aunt. I want a school for him where he will be well taught and well treated. Tell me where there is such a school."

"We have a good school here," said Mr. Wickfield. "David could not live in the school just at present; but I will tell you what you can do.—Leave him here. He is a quiet boy, and this is a quiet house. Leave him in my house."

"Thank you very much," said my aunt.

"Come and see my little housekeeper," said Mr. Wickfield. We went upstairs into a very pretty room. There was a door in the corner of it. A girl of about my own age came out and kissed Mr. Wickfield. She was very like the lady in the picture. There was a peacefulness, a calmness about her which I have never forgotten, which I shall never forget.

"This is my daughter, Agnes," said Mr. Wickfield. "Agnes, David Copperfield will stay with us; will you please show him his room?"

We all went together to see my room. Then my aunt decided to go back to Dover so as to reach it before dark. Mr. Wickfield and Agnes went away.

"Trot," my aunt said to me, as she left, "be worthy of yourself; do honour to me and to Mr. Dick, and God be with you. Never be dishonest in anything; never untrue; never be cruel.—Now I must go."

She kissed me hastily, then went out of the room, shutting the door behind her. I thought for a moment that she was angry; but I looked out into the street. I saw how sadly she got into her carriage. She had seemed angry only so as to hide her feelings.

In the evening we had dinner,—Mr. Wickfield and Agnes and I. After dinner Agnes sang; then she kissed her father good night and went to bed. I went out and walked about the city looking at the old houses and the churches. When I came back I saw Uriah Heep shutting up the office. I felt friendly to everyone, so I went and spoke to him, and when I left, I gave him my hand. How cold his hand was! I rubbed my hand afterwards so as to rub his hand off! When I went to bed his hand was still cold and wet in my mind.

Seventeen

AGNES

Next morning I went with Mr. Wickfield to the school. It was a solemn-looking building in a court-yard. I was made known to Dr. Strong, the head-master. His clothes were not well brushed nor in good order; his hair was rather long. He looked at me with cold eyes and said that he was glad to see me. Then he gave me his hand.

Sitting at work near him was a very pretty young lady whom he called Annie. I thought that she was his daughter, but when we were going into the schoolroom he spoke to her as Mrs. Strong.

We went to the schoolroom where about twenty-four boys were busy at their books. They stood up.

"A new boy, young gentlemen," said the Doctor. "His name is Trotwood Copperfield."

A boy called Adams stepped out and welcomed me. He showed me my seat.

I felt strange among these boys, for I had passed through scenes of which they knew nothing, and I knew nothing of their games and their ways. I wondered what they would think if they knew that I had lived with such people as the Micawbers, or seen me walking from London to Dover hungry and in rags.

I was unhappy and afraid of the boys in the school and hurried away as soon as school was finished. But when I came to Mr. Wickfield's house I began to feel all my unhappiness going away. I sat in my beautiful room reading until dinner-time. Then I went down. Agnes was in the sitting-room. Soon after that Mr. Wickfield came in.

"You will be happy at Dr. Strong's school," he said.

After dinner Agnes set the glasses on the table and Mr. Wickfield drank. He drank a great deal. Agnes sang. Then she sat by him and talked to him. I brought my books. She looked into them and she helped me with my work. I seem to see her now with her calm, quiet manner. I seem to hear her calm and peaceful voice as I write these words, and the goodness which she brought to me comes back again. I love Little Emily and I do not love Agnes; but I feel that there is goodness and peace and truth wherever Agnes is. . . .

Eighteen

URIAH HEEP IS HUMBLE

After dinner Mr. Wickfield went to his work. I saw a light in the office and went in. I found Uriah reading a great fat book, following every line with his finger.

"You are working late to-night, Uriah," I said.

"Yes, Master Copperfield. But I am not doing office work. I am learning Law."

"I suppose you are a great lawyer," I said, after looking at him for some time.

"Oh, no, Master Copperfield. I am a very humble[1] person. My mother is a very humble person. We live in a humble house. My father's work was very humble work: he was a sexton."[2]

"Where is he now?" I asked.

"He is in Heaven," said Uriah. "But we have much to be thankful for. I have to be thankful for living with Mr. Wickfield. I hope to become a lawyer."

"Then you will join Mr. Wickfield?" I said. "It will be Wickfield & Heep."

"Oh, no, Master Copperfield," said Uriah. "I am much too humble for that.—Your aunt is a sweet lady."

Uriah Heep had a way of moving his body from side to side when he tried to speak nicely about anyone. It was very ugly. It took my mind away from

[1] Humble = not proud.
[2] Sexton = man who keeps a church clean and also makes graves in the churchyard.

Uriah Heep made ready for going home

the nice things he was saying about my friends.

"Your aunt is a sweet lady," he said. "She admires Miss Agnes very much, doesn't she?"

"Oh, yes," I answered, not knowing what to say.

"I hope you do too. I am sure you do," said Uriah Heep.

"Everybody must admire her," I answered.

"Oh, thank you, Master Copperfield, thank you for those words. They are so true."

He seemed to tie his body into a knot and made ready for going home.

"Mother will be expecting me," he said. "If you would come and see us at our humble house mother would be very pleased."

I said that I would be glad to come.

"Perhaps you will stop here for some time, Master Copperfield? Perhaps you will take over Mr. Wickfield's business in the end?" said Uriah Heep.

"No," said I. "I do not think of that at all."

"Oh, yes, I am sure you will. I am sure you will."

He shook hands with me. His hand felt like a fish. I dreamt of it that night.

Nineteen

DR. STRONG'S SCHOOL

Dr. Strong's school was a very good school; it was very different from Mr. Creakle's. The boys were trusted by the masters. We all felt that we had a share in making the school a success. For this reason we all loved the school and wanted to do honour to it.

Some of the boys lived in Dr. Strong's house. They told me that the Doctor had been married for about a year to the beautiful young lady whom I had seen. The Doctor was writing a book, but it went on so slowly that it would not be finished within a thousand years. The Doctor was very kind to the poor. There was a story that he gave his coat to a poor woman who sold it to get drink. Then the Doctor saw his coat in a shop and bought it back again—not knowing that it was his own.

I got a letter from Peggotty. She said that Mr. and Miss Murdstone had gone away and the house had been shut up; Barkis was a good husband, but very careful with his money. Mr. Peggotty was well, and Ham and Little Emily were well. Mrs. Gummidge was not well.

My aunt came over to see me several times—always at some strange hour. I think she expected to take me by surprise, but always finding me busy she gave up these visits. I went to Dover every third or fourth week. Mr. Dick came over every other Wednesday. He always brought his writing-case and the great letter.

These Wednesdays were the happiest days in Mr. Dick's life. He soon became known to every boy in the school. He never played games with the boys; but he looked on at the games. I have often seen him standing looking at the boys playing on the ice and crying out with joy. The boys loved him. He cut fruit into strange shapes. He made boats and little carts out of all sorts of materials. He had a great respect for "The Doctor" and always stood with his hat off when he spoke to him. He and the Doctor became friends, and the Doctor began to read out from his book to Mr. Dick. Mr. Dick listened with his face shining with pleasure, but I am sure he did not understand one word of it!

Twenty

I TAKE TEA WITH URIAH HEEP

One Thursday evening I met Uriah Heep in the street.

"You promised," said he, "that you would take tea with us. I did not expect you to keep your promise, Master Copperfield; we are so very humble."

I had not decided whether I liked Uriah or hated him. But I said that I would come to tea with him.

"Mother will be very proud," said Uriah.

"Have you been studying much Law lately?" I asked.

"Oh," said Uriah, "my reading can hardly be called study. I have passed an hour or two in the evening sometimes with my law-books. I find that rather hard. There are Latin words in them which I cannot understand."

"Would you like to be taught Latin?" I asked.

"Oh, thank you, Master Copperfield," he answered. "It is very kind of you to make the offer, but I am far too humble to accept it.—Here is my humble home."

We entered a low room. There we found Mrs. Heep, who was just like Uriah, only shorter. She received me very humbly.

"This is a day to be remembered, my dear Uriah," she said, "this day on which Master Copperfield pays us a visit. My dear Uriah feared that our humbleness prevented you from coming to visit us. We are humble; we shall always be humble."

"I am sure that you have no need to be so humble," I said.

"Thank you, sir," said Mrs. Heep.

I found that Mrs. Heep slowly came nearer to me and Uriah got opposite to me, and they gave me all the best food on the table. They began to talk about their aunts; and I told them about my aunt. They talked about fathers and mothers, and I told them about my father and mother;—and then I stopped because my aunt had advised me to be silent on that subject. But I had no chance against Uriah and Mrs. Heep. They did what they liked with me. They got out of me things which I did not wish to tell. When they had learned all that they wished to learn, they began to talk about Mr. Wickfield and Agnes—how much business Mr. Wickfield did, how we passed the time after dinner, how much wine Mr. Wickfield drank— and why, and how sad it was that he took so much. I found myself telling all sorts of things which I ought not to have told.

I began to wish that I was out of the house. Then I saw a man coming down the street. The door was open. The man looked in at the door.

"Copperfield!" he said. "Is it possible?"

It was Mr. Micawber!

" My dear Copperfield, this is indeed a surprising meeting! "

I cannot say that I was glad to see Mr. Micawber there.

" I have discovered my friend Copperfield taking a meal with a lady and her son. I shall consider it an honour to be made known to them." I made Mr. Micawber known to Uriah Heep and his mother.

" We are very humble," said Mrs. Heep. " Master Copperfield has been so good as to take his tea with us. We are thankful to him."

" And what are you doing, Copperfield? "

" I am at Dr. Strong's school," I said.

I was very eager to get Mr. Micawber away.

" Shall we go and see Mrs. Micawber? " I asked.

" I should be very glad," said Mr. Micawber.

I went with Mr. Micawber to the little inn at which he was staying.

" What are you doing down in these parts? " I asked.

" I have relations here," said Mrs. Micawber, " and I had hopes that they would be able to get work for Mr. Micawber, but they did not seem glad to see us. There was only one thing to do and that was to ask my family to lend me the money with which to return to London. But we came here hoping to do something in the coal trade."

They asked me to come and have dinner with them and I could not say no. Next day I was called out of school, and I found Mr. Micawber waiting. He told me that the dinner had been arranged.

That evening I saw Mr. Micawber and Uriah Heep walking past arm-in-arm. I was not pleased to see this. When I went round to the inn next day to dinner Mr. Micawber spoke about Uriah.

"Your friend Heep," he said, "is a man of great understanding."

We had a very nice dinner. Mr. Micawber was very merry. He sang songs and we were all very friendly. I do not think I ever saw anyone happier than Mr. Micawber was that evening.

At seven o'clock next morning I received this letter:

"All is over. There is no hope of any money from Mrs. Micawber's relations. I am unable to pay what I owe. I shall soon be in prison. This is the last that you will hear from me."

I was so surprised and frightened by this sad letter that I ran away towards the little inn to see if I could help in any way; but on my way there I met the London coach with Mr. and Mrs. Micawber sitting up behind. Mr. Micawber was looking quite happy and was laughing at something that Mrs. Micawber was saying, and eating sweets out of a paper bag!

PART FOUR

THE WORLD

Twenty one

I LEAVE SCHOOL

My school days were coming to an end. My aunt and I often talked together as to what work I should do.

"This is an important matter," said my aunt. "We must not make a mistake. You must try to look at it as a man would, not as a schoolboy."

"I will, Aunt," said I.

"I think that perhaps a little change and travel may be useful to you in helping you to think and decide. You might go down and see the Peggottys."

"I should like to do that very much," I said.

I went to Canterbury to say good-bye to Agnes and Mr. Wickfield.

"I shall feel the need of you very much," I said to Agnes. "Everyone who needs you asks for your help and is guided by you, Agnes."

"Everyone is very kind to me," said Agnes.

"Whenever I get into trouble, or fall in love, I shall tell you, if you will let me," I said. "Some day I shall really fall in love."

"Oh! But you have always said that your love affairs were real," said Agnes.

"Oh! That was as a child," I said. "My wonder is that you have not fallen in love."

Agnes turned away her eyes. Then she looked up to me and said, "There is something I want to ask you. Have you noticed any change in Father?"

I had noticed it.

"Can you tell me what it is?" she said.

"I do not think he does himself any good by drinking so much," said I. "His hand shakes. He does not speak clearly, and his eyes look wild; and I have noticed that at those times when he seems to be worst, he is most likely to be wanted for some business."

"By Uriah," said Agnes.

"Yes," said I. "Then he feels that he is not fit for the business, and the next day he is worse, and the next day still worse. A few days ago I saw him with his head on the table weeping like a child."

Uriah Heep helped me to pack up my box, and I left Canterbury.

I came to London.

In the evening I went to the *theatre*. After the theatre I went back to my hotel. As I went up to bed I saw a man come in. He did not know me, but I knew him, and my old love for him flowed back into my heart.

"Steerforth!" I said. "Won't you speak to me?"

"Why! It's little Copperfield!"

"My dear Steerforth, I am very glad to see you."

"I am very glad to see you," he said. "My mother lives a little way out of London."

We met next morning at breakfast.

"Will you come and stay with me for a day or two at Highgate?" said Steerforth. "I should like you to meet my mother. She is very proud of me and talks too much about me, but you must forgive her. She will be pleased to see you."

That evening we drove up to an old brick house at Highgate on the top of the hill. An elderly[1] lady stood in the doorway. It was Steerforth's mother. She welcomed me. There was a second lady in the sitting-room. She had black hair and eager black eyes. There was a mark on her cheek—a mark of some wound made long ago. Her name was Miss Dartle, but Steerforth and his mother called her Rosa.

When we were alone I expected Steerforth to say something about Miss Dartle.

"She is very clever," I said, "isn't she?"

"Clever?" said Steerforth. "She has made herself sharper and sharper year by year. She is all edge."

"That is a strange mark on her face."

"Yes," said Steerforth. "The fact is, I did that."

"By some sad accident?"

"I was a young boy, and she made me angry. I threw a hammer at her."

"I am sorry to have spoken of such a painful subject."

"She has carried the mark ever since," said Steerforth. "She will carry it to her grave."

"I have no doubt she loves you like a brother," said I.

---

[1] Elderly = rather old.

"Well," said Steerforth, "some brothers are not loved very much, and some are loved too much."

Mrs. Steerforth seemed to love her son too much. She seemed to think and to speak of nothing else. She showed me his picture as a child, and as a boy at school as I first knew him. All the letters which he had ever written were kept in a box near her chair. She wanted to read them to me, but Steerforth asked her not to. I went up to my bedroom and there I saw a picture of Miss Dartle looking eagerly at me from above the fire. In my dreams that night there was Miss Dartle asking eager questions: "Is it really so? I want to know."

There was a servant called Littimer who was a very quiet man. He seemed to be shut up in himself like a shell-fish. Every morning when he came into my room he asked the same question.

"Mr. Steerforth would like to know how you rested."

"Thank you," said I, "very well. Is Mr. Steerforth quite well?"

"Quite well. Is there anything I can do for you, sir?"

"Nothing, thank you."

"I thank you, sir."

Then he went quietly out of the room.

68

Twenty two

STEERFORTH VISITS THE PEGGOTTYS

Steerforth decided to come with me on my visit to Yarmouth. I promised to take him to see the Peggottys in the evening, but I went first to Mr. Barkis's house. There I saw Peggotty cooking the dinner.

"Is Mr. Barkis at home?" I said.

"Yes. He is at home," said Peggotty, "but he is ill in bed."

Then she took a look at me, and stepped back.

"My dearest boy!" she said. Then we were in each other's arms.

I went up to Barkis's room. He was very pleased to see me. He lay on his back in the bed, and, as he talked, his right hand came from under the bedclothes and took a stick which lay at the side of the bed. He pushed it against a box which lay under the bed. When he felt the box his face became more peaceful.

"Old clothes," he said. "There are only old clothes in the box; I wish it was money."

·"So do I," I said.

"But it is not," said Mr. Barkis.

When we left the room, Peggotty told me that Barkis was even more careful of his money. When any money was needed he would get painfully out of bed and take some out of that box.

I met Steerforth and walked towards the Peggottys' house. They were all delighted to see us.

"Why, this is a wonderful thing," said Mr. Peggotty, "that you should want to come to this house to-night of all nights. This is the happiest of nights because Ham has asked our Little Emily to marry him."

My heart was moved to see the joy of Ham at winning the heart of this pretty little creature, and perhaps there was also pain because I still loved Little Emily. I did not quite know what to say, but Steerforth said the right words.

"Mr. Peggotty," he said, "you are a very good man and have a right to be as happy as you are to-night.—Ham, I wish you joy."

We sat round the fire and Steerforth talked to Little Emily about boats and ships and fish, and he told Mr. Peggotty how he and I had been together at Salem House. Little Emily looked and listened. Her eyes were fastened upon him.

About midnight we went away and they stood round the little doorway watching us go down the road.

"She is a beautiful little girl," said Steerforth, taking my arm. "It is a strange place and they are strange people. I found it very pleasant to mix with them. We were fortunate to have arrived in time to see their happiness. That Ham is rather an uninteresting fellow with a girl, isn't he?" said Steerforth.

These words surprised me. And then I saw that he was laughing.

"Oh, Steerforth!" I said. "You may try to hide your goodness by joking, but I know you better. I admire you for entering into the happiness of these simple people."

Twenty three

AT YARMOUTH

Steerforth and I stayed for nearly three weeks in that part of the country. We went out in the boat with Mr. Peggotty. I did not see very much of him. I spent my time going to see my old friends and the places which I knew so well. I went and saw my old home. The garden was ill cared for. Some of the trees had been cut down. One evening I came back later than usual and found Steerforth sitting alone in Mr. Peggotty's house. He was sitting in front of the fire thinking deeply. I put my hand on his shoulder and he jumped.

"Oh! " he said, "you came upon me like a spirit."

"I called you back from your dreams," I said.

"I was looking at pictures in the fire. I have been thinking that all the people we found so happy might be scattered or dead, for I sit here alone. Oh, David, I wish I had had a wise father to guide me during these last twenty years. I wish I could guide myself better."

There was something so sad in his manner that I was surprised. I asked him to tell me what was the matter, but he began to laugh.

"Oh! It is nothing—nothing," he answered. He took my arm and we went out.

"Did you know that I had bought a boat here? "

"What a strange fellow you are, Steerforth," I cried. "Why! You may never want to come near this place again."

"Oh, no," he said, "I love the place. I have bought a boat, and Mr. Peggotty will take care of it when I am not here. I must have the boat painted. I shall leave Littimer to see to it. Did you know that he has come here? "

" No," I said.

" Yes, he came this morning. I am having the boat given a new name. It is called *Storm Bird* now."

" What name are you giving it? " I asked.

" The *Little Emily*."

" Where are they all, I wonder," said I.

" See here," said Steerforth. " Here comes the original Little Emily, and Ham is with her."

When Emily saw Steerforth she took her hand away from Ham's arm, and when they walked on she did not put it back again. She seemed a little frightened and walked by herself. Suddenly a young woman passed us. It was clear that she was following Ham and Emily. She was dressed in a bold way but her clothes were poor. Her face was bold and yet full of sadness.

" Who is that black shadow following the girl? " said Steerforth. " What does it mean? Where does the woman come from, I wonder? "

We reached the inn. We had finished dinner when Littimer came and said, " Miss Mowcher is here."

" What is she doing here? " said Steerforth.

" It seems to be her part of the country, sir."

The door opened, and there came in a very small woman about forty or forty-five years of age. She took care of gentlemen's hair. She carried with her a bag from which she took a lot of bottles and other things. She attended to Steerforth's hair, talking all the time. She told stories of all the beautiful ladies whose hair she attended to.

"Ah!" she said. "There is no work around here. I have not seen a pretty woman since I have been here."

"Well," said Steerforth, "I think we could show her one."

"Yes," said I. "Her name is Emily, Miss Mowcher."

"Aha!" she said.

Her look and her way of speaking did not please me. So I said in a more serious way, "She is as good as she is beautiful, and she has promised to marry a man in her rank of life. His name is Peggotty."

"Oh!" said Miss Mowcher, "so that's it. Very well!"

She put all the bottles and other things back in her bag. Steerforth paid her. Still talking, she hurried away.

I went to Mr. Barkis's house and was surprised to find Ham walking up and down outside.

"Emily is inside," he said. "She is talking to someone whom Emily knew once, and whom she ought not to know any more—a poor woman, Master David. The people in the town think nothing of her."

"I saw her too, following you."

"Yes," said Ham. "I expect you did. After, she came under Emily's window and said: 'Emily, have pity on me. I was once as you are.' And Emily said, 'Martha, is it you?' Martha and Emily once worked together in Mr. Omer's shop. She had arranged to meet her here."

The door opened and Peggotty called Ham into the room. She had been crying, so had little Emily.

"She wants to go to London."

She held out her hand to Ham, and Ham gave her a bag of money. Then Martha stood up. She tried to speak, but could not. She went away weeping.

Twenty four

A MERRY PARTY

My aunt had arranged for me to work in the office of some lawyers, Spenlow & Jorkins, in London, and paid them money to let me learn the business.

I now had rooms of my own near their office. It was wonderful to have a new place all of one's own. But sometimes I felt very much alone. One morning Steerforth came in.

"My dear Steerforth," I said, "I thought I should never see you again. Will you stay and have some breakfast?"

"No, no!" said Steerforth. "I can't. I have promised to meet some friends."

"You will come back to dinner?" I said.

"No, I can't. I must stay with those two fellows."

"Bring your friends here to dinner," I said.

He agreed to do this.

We had a very merry dinner-party. The wine passed faster and faster. I became merrier and merrier. I made a speech and Steerforth made a speech. I drank to the health of everyone. Then we went to the theatre. In the theatre I saw Agnes. When she looked at me there was a look of sadness and wonder in her face.

"Agnes!" I said. "Well! Well! Why, it is Agnes!"

"Silence!" she said. "Don't make such a noise."

"Agnes," I said.

"I am afraid you are not well," she answered. "Listen, are you going away soon?"

"Am I going away soon?" I said in a foolish voice. "Yes! Yes!"

"Listen!" said Agnes, "I know you will do as I ask. Come away now. Ask your friends to take you home."

Next morning as I was coming out of my house I received a letter from Agnes.

MY DEAR TROTWOOD,

I am staying with Mr. and Mrs. Waterbrook at Ealing Place, Holborn. Will you come and see me to-day?

I wrote five or six answers to this letter, trying to say how sorry I was for what had happened in the theatre. And then I wrote:

DEAR AGNES,

I will come at four o'clock.

At four o'clock I entered the room where Agnes was sitting. She looked so quiet and good.

"I wish you had not seen me, Agnes," I said.. "If it had been anyone but you!"

She put her hand on my arm.

"Sit down. Don't be unhappy. If you can't trust me, whom can you trust?"

"Oh, Agnes," I said, "you are such a good friend to me!"

"If I am your good friend, Trotwood," she said, "there is one thing I wish to do. I wish to warn you against your worst enemy. I mean Steerforth. He has a very bad effect on you."

"My dear Agnes," I said, "you wrong him. It is unjust to judge him for what you saw a few nights ago."

"I don't judge him from that. I judge him from many things.

"You must not forget me," said Agnes. "You must always tell me whenever you get into trouble, or whenever you fall in love."

Then she asked me if I had seen Uriah. "I believe he's going to become my father's partner,"[1] she said.

"What! " I said. "Will that fellow become your father's partner? "

"Yes," said Agnes. "I am afraid that is forced upon him. My father is afraid of him. He has power over my father. Oh, Trotwood, I feel as if I had been my father's enemy, instead of his friend. He has made the circle of his love and duty smaller and smaller, so that his whole mind is given to me. His thoughts have been turned too much upon one idea and this has weakened him. I have been the cause of his fall."

A few days later I went to a party at the Waterbrooks'. Uriah was there. He kept close to me all the time. He was close to me when I went away. Agnes had asked me to be nice to him, so I asked him to come up to my room. I gave him coffee.

"Oh, Master Copperfield! " he said. "To see you

---

[1] One who has a share in a business is called a partner.

Uriah Heep and Agnes

waiting on me and bringing me coffee is more than I could have expected. But so many things have happened which I have not expected. I hope that I may be able to do good to Mr. Wickfield. He has been so unwise. If anyone else had been in my place during the last few years he would have had Mr. Wickfield in his power."

He closed his long hand as if he held Mr. Wickfield in it. I hated him.

"Miss Agnes was looking very beautiful to-night," said Uriah.

"She looked as she always does, nobler and more beautiful than anyone around her," I answered.

"Oh, thank you," said Uriah.

"There is no reason why you should thank me," said I.

"I have a secret to tell you," said Uriah. "Although I am so humble, I love the ground my Agnes walks upon."

I could have killed him as he said the words.

"She loves her father very much, and I hope that she may for his sake be kind to me," said Uriah.

I understood his plan. He meant to use his power over Mr. Wickfield to force him to give him Agnes as his wife.

"There is no need to hurry," said Uriah. "My Agnes is very young still."

Uriah slept on a chair in my sitting-room. I dreamed of Agnes that night. She seemed to be praying me to save her. When I awoke I went into the next room and saw Uriah lying there with his legs out and his mouth open, and I could have killed him.

Twenty five

DORA

Each day I went to Mr. Spenlow's office to work there. After some time Mr. Spenlow asked me to come out to his house in the country.

"Where is Miss Dora?" he said to a servant as we entered.

"Dora!" I thought. "What a beautiful name!"

We went into a room near by.

"Mr. Copperfield, my daughter Dora."

I looked up and saw her and loved her madly.

"And this," said Mr. Spenlow, "is my daughter's friend."

"I have seen Mr. Copperfield before."

It was Miss Murdstone!

Early next morning I walked in the garden. As I was walking there I came round the corner and saw Dora.

"You are out early, Miss Spenlow," I said.

"Yes," she said. "On Sunday morning I do not do my music lesson. The morning is the brightest time in the day."

"This morning is very bright for me," I said.

A little dog came running along the path. Dora took him in her arms. I thought how fortunate the dog was. We had a quiet day. We went for a walk, and in the evening we looked at books and pictures. When I said good night to Mr. Spenlow, he did not know that I was thinking of him as my future father-in-law.

Twenty six

STEERFORTH RETURNS

Mr. and Mrs. Micawber came to supper with me in my room. It was a very merry party. I had met Traddles, my old school friend at Salem House, and he joined us. We were at the height of our enjoyment when a man came into the room. It was Littimer.[1]

"What is the matter?" I asked.

"I ask your pardon, sir. I was told to come in."

"Is your master here?" said I.

"No."

"Have you not seen him here?"

"I ask your pardon," said Littimer.

"Is Mr. Steerforth coming up from Oxford?"

"I think he may be here to-morrow," said Littimer, not answering my question.

"Oh, Littimer, did you remain long at Yarmouth?"

"No. Not very long, sir."

"You saw the boat finished?"

"Yes, sir."

"Has Mr. Steerforth seen it yet?"

"I really can't say, sir. I wish you good night."

We were all happier when he had gone. I did not trust the man. Our party came to an end. I went back to my fire and was thinking about Mr. and Mrs. Micawber when I heard a step coming up the stairs. At first I thought it was Traddles. And then I knew. It was Steerforth.

[1] See page 67.

"Why!" he cried. "Have I found you feasting again? I met your guests outside all talking loudly in your praise."

I offered Steerforth some food and he sat down at the table.

"Here is a supper good enough for a king," he said. "It will do me good. I have come from Yarmouth."

"I thought you had come from Oxford."

"No," said Steerforth. "I have been out in my boat. I have a letter for you. Old Mr. Barkis is very ill."

I read the letter.

"I think I will go down and see them," I said.

Steerforth turned to go.

"Good night, my dear Steerforth," I said. "I shall go to-morrow morning."

"Good night."

He stood there with one hand on each of my shoulders.

"If anything should separate us," he said, "you must think of me at my best."

"You were always best to me," I said.

"God bless you," he answered, "and good night."

Twenty seven

BARKIS GOES OUT WITH THE TIDE

I reached Yarmouth. Peggotty took me in her arms and thanked me again and again for being such a comfort to her. Then she asked me to come upstairs.

"Mr. Barkis always liked you. He often talked of

you. He is asleep now, but if he wakes up he will be glad to see you. It will make him brighter."

It did not seem to me that anything could make Barkis brighter. He was lying with his head and shoulders out of bed half resting on the box of which he thought so much. He was too weak to feel it with the stick which he had used before. So he put the box on a chair by his bedside. Time and the world were slipping away from him. But the box was there and the last words he said were "Old clothes."

"Barkis, my dear," said Peggotty, "here is Master David. Won't you speak to Master David?"

But he was silent and senseless as the box. He was going out with the tide.[1] We stood there watching him. The sea went out over the sand; and as it went, life slowly passed away from him. He began to talk: something about driving to school. Then he opened his eyes and said to me clearly with a pleasant smile, "Barkis is willing."

The sea had gone out. He went out with the tide.

Twenty eight

EMILY HAS GONE!

Rain was falling as I walked towards Peggotty's house, and the moon was behind the clouds. I saw a light shining in the window. Soon I was at the door. Mr. Peggotty was smoking by the fire. Peggotty

---

[1] Tide = movement of the sea caused by the moon.

was sitting mending clothes, and Mrs. Gummidge was in the corner.

"Well, Peggotty," I said, "how are you?"

"She's easy in her mind," said Mr. Peggotty. "She did her duty to Barkis, and he has done his duty to her, and it's all right."

He took a candle, lit it, and set it in the window.

"That is for our Little Emily," he said. "She sees it on her way home from work. But when she is married and gone I shall put the candle there just the same, and sit in front of the fire pretending I am expecting her, as I am doing now. As I see that candle burn up I say she is looking at it and she is coming, and I am right. Here she is!"

It was only Ham.

"Where is Emily?" said Mr. Peggotty.

Ham made a movement of his head as if she were outside.

Then Ham said, "Master David, will you come out for a minute and see what Emily and I have got to show you?"

As I passed him at the door I saw that his face was white. He pushed me into the open air and shut the door.

"Ham, what is the matter?"

"Master David!" he cried. And he wept.

"Ham, poor fellow, tell me; what is the matter?"

"My love, Master David. The pride and hope of my heart. Little Emily has gone!"

"Gone?"

"She has run away. What am I to say to them in there?"

The door opened and Mr. Peggotty looked out. I shall never forget the change which came over his face as he saw us. I shall never forget the crying and the women hanging about him. I stood in the room with the paper which Ham had given to me.

"Read it, sir," he said.

In a silence of death I read:

"When you, who love me so much, see this, I shall be far away. I shall never come back unless he brings me back—a lady.

"Tell my uncle I have never loved him so much. Be his comfort. Love some good girl who will be true to you. God bless all. I pray for you all often on my knees. If he does not bring me back a lady, I won't pray for myself, but I will pray for all."

Mr. Peggotty slowly moved his eyes from my face as if he was waking from a dream.

Then he said in a low voice, "Who is the man? I want to know his name."

"Master David," said Ham in a broken voice, "I don't blame you. But his name is Steerforth."

Mr. Peggotty gave no cry. He took down his coat from the corner.

"Now give me that hat," he said.

Ham asked him where he was going.

"I am going to look for Emily," he said. "I am going first to break that boat. Then I am going to look for Emily."

"Where?" said Ham.

"Anywhere. I am going to look for her through the world. I am going to find her and bring her back."

Twenty-nine

MR. PEGGOTTY AND MRS. STEERFORTH

Next morning I went to London. Mr. Peggotty came with me. He meant to see Mrs. Steerforth. In order to help him I wrote to Mrs. Steerforth and told her what his wrong was; I told her that he was a common man, but very gentle and good, and that I hoped she would see him.

When he went into the room Mrs. Steerforth was sitting in her chair; Rosa Dartle was standing behind her. The lady looked steadily at Peggotty, and he looked at her. She made a sign to Peggotty to sit down.

"No," said he, "I will stand." He took out Emily's letter and gave it to her.

"Please read that, madam."

She read it.

"'Unless he brings me back a lady,'" said Mr. Peggotty, pointing to those words in the letter. "I have come to ask whether he has kept his promise."

"No," said the lady.

"Why not?" said Mr. Peggotty.

"It is impossible. She is far below him."

"Raise her up," said Mr. Peggotty.

"She is untaught, unschooled."

"Teach her," said Mr. Peggotty.

"Her family is too humble."

"Listen!" he said. "You know what it is to love your child; and so do I. You do not know what it is to lose your child; but we will all promise never to see her again; we will think of her as far away and trust her to her husband."

"It is impossible. Such a marriage would spoil my son's chances in life. It would ruin him.—If there is anything else that I can give——"

"Do you offer me money? That is almost worse than your son's act."

She changed now. Her face was angry.

Miss Dartle touched her and bent down her head and whispered to her.

"No, Rosa! Not a word." She stood up.

"No, madam, do not trouble yourself," said Mr. Peggotty. "I have no more to say. I came here with no hope and I take away no hope."

As we went out Rosa Dartle came. She spoke to me:

"Why did you bring this man here?" Her face was black with anger. "Don't you know that Mrs. Steerforth and her son are both mad with their pride? Why do you bring this man here? He and his girl, they are bad, worthless people. I would have the girl's face marked with fire. I would have her thrown into the street. I would hunt her to her death."

I have seen anger in many forms. I have never seen such anger as hers.

When I joined Mr. Peggotty he was walking slowly down the hill.

"Where are you going?" I asked.

"I am going to look for her, far and wide. If any hurt has come to her, remember the last words which I left for her—*My love is unchanged, and I forgive her.*"

PART FIVE

MARRIAGE

Thirty

ENGAGED TO BE MARRIED

Mr. Spenlow told me that in one week's time was Dora's birthday and he would be glad if I would come and join him and his family.

I set out early in the morning and reached the house. Dora was in the garden and with her was a friend called Miss Julia Mills. Jip, the dog, was there. As we went out into the country I thought of nothing but Dora; the sunshine was Dora; the birds sang "Dora."

We sat under the trees and had a meal, and after that Dora sang. We had tea, and in the evening I rode home by Dora's side.

Just as I was going away Miss Mills said to me, "Mr. Copperfield, I want to speak to you. . . . Dora is coming to stay with us. I hope you will come and visit us."

A few days later I went to Miss Mills's house. I had decided to ask Dora to marry me. Miss Mills and Dora were in the room. After a short time Miss Mills got up and went out. I do not know how I told Dora of my love. I did it in a moment. I told her that I should die without her.

Dora and I were engaged.[1]

Thirty-one

RUINED

I went to see my old friend Traddles. I came back to my room with Peggotty. When I got there I was surprised to find the door open and I heard voices inside. I went and found my aunt and Mr. Dick! My aunt was sitting on a lot of boxes; Mr. Dick was holding a big kite.

" My dear Aunt! " I cried. " This is an unexpected pleasure. You remember my aunt, Peggotty? "

" Hallo," said my aunt to Peggotty. " How are you? Don't call the woman by that odd name. She has married and got another name. What is your name now? "

" Barkis," said Peggotty.

" Well, that is better. How do you do, Barkis."

We had tea. From time to time I saw my aunt looking at me strangely. I wondered what the reason of this was. I had not told her about Dora. Was that it?

" Trot," said my aunt at last, when she had finished tea, " Trot, you must be firm and trust your own strength."

" Yes, Aunt."

" Why do you think I am sitting on all these boxes? "

" I don't know," I said.

[1] Engaged = promised to marry each other.

"Because," said my aunt, "they are all that I have! I am ruined, my dear."

If the house and every one of us in it had fallen into the river, I could not have been more surprised.

"Dick knows it," said my aunt. "I am ruined. All that I have in the world is in this room. Barkis, I want to get a bed for this gentleman to-night. Anything will do."

Then she put her arms round my neck and said that she was sorry only for me. In another moment she hid her feelings and said:

"We must meet troubles boldly, and not let them frighten us. We must live through our troubles, Trot."

Thirty-two

AGNES COMES

Next morning I decided that the first thing which I ought to do was to set myself free from Spenlow & Jorkins and get back the money which my aunt had paid them. I sat in a corner of the office thinking about Dora until Mr. Spenlow came in.

"How are you, Copperfield?" he said. "It is a nice morning, isn't it?"

"Yes, a beautiful morning," said I. "May I talk to you before you go into court?"[1]

"Why, yes," said he. "Come into my room."

I followed him into the room.

"I am sorry to say that I have some bad news from

[1] Into the law-court. Mr. Spenlow was a lawyer.

my aunt. She has lost all her money. I wish to end my work here and to get back from you the money which she paid you."

"I am very sorry," said Mr. Spenlow, "but that is not possible. If I were free, I could have arranged it, but there is Mr. Jorkins."

"Do you think that, if I spoke to Mr. Jorkins, he would do anything?"

"Oh, no," said Mr. Spenlow. "Mr. Jorkins would not agree to such a thing."

I went up to Mr. Jorkins's room. I told him what I wanted.

"You have spoken to Mr. Spenlow, I suppose?" said Mr. Jorkins. "If Mr. Spenlow does not agree, I cannot agree. I'm sorry."

"But he said that he could agree, but you——"

"Well, if he does not agree to it, I cannot agree."

I could not discover between Mr. Spenlow and Mr. Jorkins which was the one who did not agree!

As I walked along the street I heard a carriage coming behind me. Then I saw a beautiful face—the face of Agnes.

"Agnes," I cried, "oh, my dear Agnes. What a pleasure it is to see you! Where are you going?"

"I am going to see your aunt," said she. She got out of her carriage and we walked together.

"I am not alone," she said. "My father is with me, and Uriah Heep."

"They are not partners?" said I. "Curse him!"

"Yes," said Agnes. "He has such power over my father! There is such a change in the house that you would not know it. Uriah and his mother live with us now. The chief evil of their being in the house is that I cannot be as near Father as I could wish. Uriah Heep is between us. But if wrong is being done, I hope that simple love and truth will be stronger in the end."

We found my aunt alone. She told Agnes about her losses.

"What is to be done?" she said at last. "The cottage will give us seventy pounds a year. Dick has a hundred pounds, but that will be used for himself."

"Dr. Strong has left his school," said Agnes, "and has come to live in London. He would like to have someone to help him with the book which he is writing. Trotwood may work for him."

"Dear Agnes," I cried, "you are always my good friend."

So I sat down and wrote a letter to Dr. Strong and asked to see him next day at ten o'clock.

Wherever Agnes was there was always some sign of her sweet presence. When I came back I found my aunt's birds hanging in the window, my chair had been put near the window just as my aunt's chair had stood. Just as I was looking round at this I heard a knock on the door.

"I think," said Agnes, "that is Father."

I opened the door. Mr. Wickfield and Uriah Heep came in. Mr. Wickfield was much changed. There was an unhealthy redness in his face; his hand shook. It seemed terrible to me that he should have lost his power; that he should be dependent on that creeping creature Uriah Heep. It was as if a monkey were in charge of a man.

"Well, Wickfield," said my aunt. "I've been telling your daughter how well I have been dealing with my money. I have been asking the advice of Agnes. I think she is the best person in the firm."[1]

"I should be happy," said Uriah Heep, "if Miss Agnes was a partner."

"You are a partner yourself," said my aunt, "and that ought to be enough for you. How are you getting on?"

This was said in a very rough voice.

Mr. Heep answered that he was getting on well enough.

"If there is anything that we can do to help, if Mother or I myself or Wickfield can do anything we shall be really glad," said Uriah.

"Uriah Heep," said Mr. Wickfield in a low voice, "is active in the business. I agree with what he says."

"Oh, how wonderful it is to be so trusted!" said Uriah.

"Are you going, Father?" said Agnes. "Will you walk back with Trotwood and me?"

"I have business to do," said Uriah; "so I will leave Mr. Wickfield with you."

We sat there talking about our happy days at Canterbury. Mr. Wickfield, left with Agnes, soon became more like his old self.

We had dinner together. Agnes sat beside him and poured out his wine. When it was dark he lay down. As Agnes came from him towards the window I could see tears in her eyes.

[1] Firm = business company.

I pray that I may never forget the dear girl. She filled my heart with thoughts of good. She strengthened my weakness, and now she spoke to me about Dora; listened to my praises of her—praised her again. Oh, Agnes, sister of my boyhood. If I had known then what I knew long afterwards! —There was a beggar in the street, and as I passed he said, "Blind! Blind! Blind! "

I went along the Highgate Road full of new life and new purposes. I had decided to offer to work for Dr. Strong in the mornings and evenings so as to have more money for my married life. On my way to visit him I saw a cottage which was to be sold. I went into it and looked at it. There was a little garden for Jip the dog. It would do well for Dora and me.

I found the Doctor's house and saw him walking in the garden. I went in.

"Why, my dear Copperfield," said the Doctor, "I am very pleased to see you. As to your idea of working for me, it is very pleasing; but do you not think you could do something better? Seventy pounds a year is very little."

"It is twice what I have, Dr. Strong," I said. "I will come to you mornings and evenings."

The Doctor was very happy at the idea of our working together at his dictionary. His pockets were full of pieces of paper all about his work. We decided to begin at seven o'clock the next morning.

Just about this time I received a letter from Mr. Micawber asking me to come and see him at his room in London. "You will be surprised," he wrote, "to hear that something has turned up."

When I arrived I found the two young Micawbers on a bed in the sitting-room, and Mr. Micawber getting ready some strong drink.

"I am going," said Mr. Micawber, "to Canterbury. I have been asked by my friend Uriah Heep to help him in his business. My friend Heep is a man of great powers of mind; he will not pay me very much, but he will free me from my debts."

I was surprised at this news and wondered what it meant.

"I believe," said Mrs. Micawber, "that if Micawber gives his mind to the Law he may rise very high. He might even become a judge. I am afraid that, by starting so low, he may make it hard for himself to rise. Do you think that Mr. Micawber might become a judge?"

"He might," I answered.

Thirty-three

I TELL DORA

My new life had lasted for more than a week. I was working very hard. Dora did not yet know of the loss of my aunt's money, nor of the work I was doing. I went to see her.

She came into the sitting-room with Jip running and jumping behind her. I asked her:

"Do you think that you can love a beggar?"

"How can you ask such a foolish question?"

"Dora, my dearest, I am a beggar! I am ruined."

"If you say such foolish things, I shall make Jip bite you."

But I looked so serious that Dora put her hand on my shoulder and began to cry. I fell on my knees and begged her not to break my heart. I told her that I loved her. "Do you still love me, Dora?"

"Oh, yes," said Dora. "Oh, yes. But don't frighten me by talking about being poor and working hard."

"May I say something?" I asked.

"Oh, please, don't——"

"If you would remember that you will be married to a poor man. Look at your father's account books and learn a little about money. It will be useful afterwards."

Then she began to cry again, and called for Miss Mills. Miss Mills came. I asked whether she could in any way draw Dora's mind towards a cookery book[1] or an account book. She promised to try, but was not very hopeful.

Thirty-four

MR. SPENLOW FINDS OUT

One day when I went to the office I found Mr. Spenlow looking very grave. When I said "good morning" he looked at me coldly and asked me to come with him to an inn near the place.

[1] Cookery book = book about cooking.

I went with him into an upstairs room and there I saw Miss Murdstone.

"Will you please show Mr. Copperfield what you have in your bag?" said Mr. Spenlow.

Miss Murdstone took out my last letter to Dora.

"I believe that it is your writing, Mr. Copperfield?" said Mr. Spenlow.

"It is," I answered.

"I believe those other letters were also written by you," said Mr. Spenlow.

"Yes."

"Will you go on, Miss Murdstone?" said Mr. Spenlow.

"I had an idea," said Miss Murdstone, "that there was something going on between Mr. Copperfield and Miss Spenlow. I decided to watch carefully. Last evening, after tea, I saw the dog playing with a piece of paper. I caught the dog and got the paper. I saw what it was and asked Miss Spenlow if she had any other letters and at last got from her those which I have shown you."

"Have you anything to say in answer?" said Mr. Spenlow.

"I have nothing to say," I answered, "except that the blame was mine."

"Take those letters and throw them in the fire," said Mr. Spenlow. "Give me Miss Spenlow's letters and I will throw them in the fire."

I would not agree.

"You perhaps know that I am a rich man and that my daughter is my nearest relation. I do not wish to have to change the arrangements which I have made. Take a week to think over what I have said."

I went back to the office. I thought of running out madly to Dora's house. I wrote a letter to Mr. Spenlow begging him to be gentle with Dora, and put it on his table.

I went to see Miss Mills. She had a wonderful flow of words and liked to pour them out, and she made me feel more unhappy than before.

I told my aunt, but she gave me no hope. I went to bed in despair. On Saturday morning I went to the office. I saw a number of men standing round the door. I went in. There was old Tiffey, the clerk, with his hat in his hand sitting on someone else's chair.

"This is a fearful thing, Mr. Copperfield," he said.

"What is? What is the matter?"

"Mr. Spenlow!"

"Well?"

"Dead. He fell out of his carriage."

Thirty-five

URIAH SAYS TOO MUCH

I went down to Canterbury and visited Mr. Wickfield's house. In the little room where Uriah Heep once worked, I now found Mr. Micawber.

"How do you like the Law, Mr. Micawber?" I asked.

"A man of my powers of imagination finds that the Law demands too much dealing with facts."

"How do you like the law, Mr. Micawber?"

"Does he pay you well?" I asked.

"He has paid off all my debts—most kindly, most fully."

"I should not have expected him to be free with his money," I said.—"Do you see much of Mr. Wickfield?"

"Not much. He is a man who means well, but he is of no further use."

"I think that his partner tries to make him useless," said I.

"My dear Copperfield, I am here as a trusted servant and there are some matters about which I cannot speak freely."

I saw a change in Mr. Micawber. There was something between him and me, something which made it difficult for us to be as friendly as we had been in the past.

I found Agnes sitting in her room.

"Oh, Agnes," I said, "I have felt the need of you so much lately. You used to think for me; I came naturally to you for advice and support. When I am with you there is something which changes me so much for the better. What is your secret, Agnes? My trust is in you."

"But it must not be in me, Trotwood," said Agnes. "It must be in Dora now."

That evening we sat at dinner. Mr. Wickfield drank to the health of my aunt, and to Mr. Dick. Then Uriah stood up.

"I will drink," said he, "to the fairest lady in the land."

Mr. Wickfield had his empty glass in his hand. He

looked up at the mother's picture; then he put his hand to his head.

"I am too humble to drink to her health, but I admire her. I love her," said Uriah.

Mr. Wickfield's hands were pressed together in his pain.

"To be the father of Agnes Wickfield is a proud thing, but to be her husband——" continued Uriah.

May I never again hear such a cry as that which her father gave.

"What is the matter?" said Uriah. "Are you mad?"

I put my arms round Mr. Wickfield begging him to be calm. He was mad for the moment. At last he became calm.

"Look at him!" he cried, pointing to Uriah. "Because of him I have given up step by step my good name, my peace and quiet, my house and home."

"Don't be foolish, Mr. Wickfield," said Uriah. "There's no harm done."

"I thought that I could trust him because it was in his interest to be true to me, but see what he is!"

"You had better stop him, Copperfield," said Uriah. "He will say something for which he will be sorry afterwards."

"I'll say anything!" cried Mr. Wickfield. "Why should I not say what I like?"

"Be careful, I tell you!" said Uriah to me. "If you don't stop him talking, you are not his friend. You and I know what we know, don't we? Can't you see that I am humble? If I've said too much, I am sorry."

"Oh, Trotwood, Trotwood," cried Mr. Wickfield,

"what have I come down to since I first saw you in this house. Weakness has ruined me. I have been weak in remembering—in remembering my child's mother too much. My natural grief has turned to disease. I have thought it possible to love one creature in the world and not love the rest. Weak in my grief, weak in my love, weak in my escape from the darker side of both. Oh, see the ruin that I am, and hate me! "

He fell into a chair and wept.

It was dark when I got up on a coach at the inn door. Uriah came to the side of the coach.

"Copperfield," he said in a low voice like a frog's, "I thought you'd be glad to hear that there's no more trouble between us. I've been to his room and we've made everything right. I suppose you have sometimes taken an apple from the tree before it was ready?— But the time will come. I can wait! "

Thirty-six

DORA'S COOKERY BOOK

I saw much of Dora, but one thing troubled me— this was that Dora seemed by all to be treated as a pretty plaything. My aunt always called her Little Blossom. Her aunt, Miss Lavinia, treated her in the same way. I decided to speak to Dora about this.

"I wish I could get them to behave differently," I said, "because you know, my dear, you are not a child."

"There! " said Dora, "you are going to be angry

with me. They are all very kind to me and I am very happy."

"Well, you might be happy and yet be treated differently."

"You ought not to be cruel to me, dearest."

She asked me to give her a cookery book, and I was delighted. I also gave her an old account book. But the cookery book gave her a headache[1] and the accounts made her cry. I tried to teach her myself.

"Now suppose, dearest, that we were married and you were going to buy me a piece of meat for dinner, would you know how to buy it?"

"Why, the meat-seller would know how to sell it! So what need I know?" said Dora.

"Suppose I said that I would like a nice Irish stew[2] for dinner, what would you do?"

"I should tell the servant to make it," said Dora.

So the chief use of the cookery book was to be put down in a corner as a thing for Jip to stand on.

Thirty-seven

THE CHILD-WIFE

Dora and I were married. We were in our cottage with Mary Ann, the servant.

"My dear," said I one day, "has Mary Ann no idea of time? Dinner should be at four, but it is now five."

[1] Headache = pain in the head.
[2] Irish stew = meat and vegetables cooked together in water.

" Perhaps the clock is fast.—And I dare not speak to her. I am afraid of her."

" I was forced to go out yesterday when dinner was half finished. On the day before that the meat was not properly cooked. To-day I get no dinner at all. I do not wish to blame you, my dear, but this is not comfortable."

" Oh, you cruel boy, to say that I am a bad wife."

The next trouble was the trouble of servants. When Mary Ann left us I found that some teaspoons and some money were missing. After her came Mrs. Kidgerbury who was too old to do any work, then another servant who broke everything, then a number of servants who did not know their work, then a young woman who wore Dora's hat when she went out with a friend.

Everyone seemed to deceive us. As soon as we came into a shop the people brought out their worst goods. All our fish was bad, our meat was hard; our bread was soft and wet. We seemed to use enough butter to cover the whole floor of the house. The women who washed our clothes sold them; the servants bought things for themselves at the shops, and let us pay for them. A friend came to dinner and the food could not be eaten.

That evening, after my friend had gone, Dora came and sat down by my side.

" I am sorry," she said. " I wish, before I was married, that I could have lived with Agnes for a whole year.—Will you call me a name that I want you to call me? "

" What is it? " I said.

"Call me Child-wife. When you are going to be angry with me, say to yourself, 'It is only my child-wife.' "

Thirty-eight

FORMING DORA'S MIND

I had been married about a year and a half. After many attempts we had given up keeping house. The house kept itself. We had a boy and the cook. The chief work of the boy seemed to be to quarrel with the cook. He stole Dora's watch and sold it. He was taken to prison, and before the judge told of other things which he had stolen. He also told about the cook. I felt so ashamed of being so stolen from that I would have paid him to be silent.

All this led to some serious thought and I spoke to Dora one evening:

"My love, it seems to me that our lack of management does harm not only to ourselves but to other people. We seem to make people become thieves. I begin to feel that these people become bad because we are not being very good ourselves."

"Oh! Oh! " cried Dora, "what a thing to say! Did you ever see me stealing gold watches? " She began to cry.

"Now, Dora, my love, I must ask you to listen. We must learn to act rightly to those whom we employ. I am afraid we give chances to people to do wrong. I feel unhappy about this."

But Dora cried, "If you are unhappy why did you marry me? Why don't you send me away to my aunt in Putney? or Julia Mills in India?"—It was useless to talk to her any more.

I decided to "form Dora's mind." I began at once. I talked about serious subjects; I read Shakespeare to her. I told her useful pieces of knowledge. But Dora seemed to guess what I was doing and seemed to fear it. She hated Shakespeare. I went on for some months, but the forming of Dora's mind was not a success. I began to think that perhaps it was already formed.

So I bought her some jewels for her ears and said that I feared we had not been very good company for each other these last few months. "The truth is, Dora, that I have been trying to be wise."

"And to make me wise too?" said Dora. "Haven't you?"

I nodded.

"It is of no use. You know what I wanted you to call me—Child-wife."

Our mind and purposes did not fit. I had tried to fit Dora to myself. I would now try to fit myself to Dora. This made the second year much happier than the first. But as the year went on, Dora was not strong. I had hoped that a baby would come and that its hands, lighter than mine, would help form Dora's character. It was not to be.

I carried Dora downstairs in the morning and up-stairs at night with Jip running behind and in front of me. But sometimes when I took her up in my arms she seemed lighter than usual.

"Good night, Little Blossom," said my aunt.

Little Blossom was so soon to fade and die.

Dora had been ill for many weeks. I had got so used to her being ill. Jip seemed suddenly to have become old. Dora lay smiling, and beautiful, and said no complaining word. She said that we were very good to her.

.   .   .   .

I sat in the quiet shaded room with the face of my child-wife turned towards me and her fingers in my hand. She was dead.

PART SIX

SETTLEMENT

Thirty-nine

MR. MICAWBER SPEAKS

I received a strange letter from Mr. Micawber. "My peace is ended. My power of enjoyment is destroyed. The flower is faded."—And so it went on. I read the letter several times but could not get its meaning; and yet it seemed to be more important than most of Mr. Micawber's letters.

At the same time I received a letter from Mrs. Micawber:

"Mr. Micawber is not himself. He is saying that he has sold himself to the Devil. He says that he wishes to be separated from me. He is secret and strange in his manner. I beg you to see him and talk to him."

I wrote a comforting letter to Mrs. Micawber and arranged to meet Mr. Micawber at my aunt's house.

We found Mr. Micawber in very low spirits.

"I hope it is not because you have begun to dislike the Law," I said.

He did not answer.

"How is our friend Heep?" I asked.

"If you ask about him as your friend, I am sorry.

If you ask about him as my friend, I laugh! I do not wish to speak about the subject of Heep.—Oh, leave me; leave me to walk the earth as an outcast.[1] Death will settle my business soon enough."

"I hope that Mrs. Micawber and your family are well, sir," said my aunt.

"They are as well, madam, as outcasts[1] can ever hope to be," answered Mr. Micawber.

"Mr. Micawber," said I, "speak out. You are among friends. What is the matter?"

"What is the matter?—Evil is the matter! Wrong-doing is the matter. Thieving and deceiving are the matter! And the cause of all of it is HEEP!—The struggle is over! I will live this life no longer. Give me back my wife, my family. I will take no man's hand until I have broken to pieces that creature—HEEP!—In one week's time—at the hotel in Canterbury—tell all.—Go now."

I have never seen a man so excited. He ran out of the house.

A letter was brought, written at an inn nearby.

SIR,

I ask to be pardoned for my excitement. I hope that I made plain the fact that I shall meet you at the Ship Inn in Canterbury in one week's time.

WILKINS MICAWBER.

In a week's time my aunt, Mr. Dick and I went to Canterbury and found a note waiting for us in the inn telling us to expect Mr. Micawber at half-past

[1] Outcast = a person cast out from the company of his fellow men.

nine on the next morning in the office of Wickfield & Heep.

We found Mr. Micawber at his desk, writing—or pretending to write.

"How do you do, Mr. Micawber?" said I.

"Mr. Copperfield," said Mr. Micawber gravely, "I hope I see you well. Mr. Wickfield is ill in bed, but Miss Wickfield will be happy to see her old friends."

He opened the door of the sitting-room and said:

"Miss Trotwood, Mr. David Copperfield and Mr. Dick."

I could see that our visit surprised Uriah Heep, but a moment later he was as humble as ever.

"Well," he said, "this is an unexpected pleasure. Things are changed in this office, Miss Trotwood, since I was a humble clerk."

Agnes came in. She seemed anxious and tired. Uriah watched her while she greeted us.

"Don't wait, Micawber," said Uriah.—"What are you waiting for? Micawber! Did you hear me tell you not to wait?"

"Yes," said Mr. Micawber, without moving.

"Then why do you wait?"

"Because I wish to!" said Mr. Micawber.

Uriah's cheeks became pale.[1]

"If there is a scoundrel[2] upon earth that scoundrel's name is HEEP."

Uriah fell back as if he had been struck.

"Oh! This has been planned. You have arranged to meet here. You have been getting at my clerk, Copper-

---

[1] Pale = white.
[2] Scoundrel = bad man.

field! Now, take care. You'll make nothing of this. We understand each other—and we don't love each other. Micawber, go! I'll talk to you later."

My friend Traddles came in leading Mrs. Heep.
"Who are you?" said Uriah.
"I am a friend of Mr. Wickfield," said Traddles, "and I have power to act for him."
"Uriah," said Mrs. Heep.
"Be silent!" cried Uriah.—I always knew that his humbleness was unreal!
Mr. Micawber stood up and took out a large piece of paper. He began to read:

"The business of Wickfield & Heep was done by Heep alone. Heep did everything: and Heep is a thief."

Uriah ran forward and tried to seize the letter, but Mr. Micawber struck his hand so that it fell, as if broken.
"The Devil take you!" said Uriah.
"Come near me again and I'll break your head," said Micawber. He went on reading.

"I was paid twenty-two shillings a week; the rest was made to depend on the value of my work—and that meant on the baseness of my name, on the wrong I was able to do for Heep. He lent me money, and this put me still further in his power. I found that my services were needed to help him in deceiving Mr. Wickfield."

Mr. Micawber looked round to see the effect of his words. Then he continued:

"Mr. Wickfield was deceived in every way while Heep was saying all the time how grateful he was to him, how much he was his friend.—At last my heart was changed, changed by the thought of Miss Wickfield. I began to look into things secretly. He got Mr. Wickfield to sign important papers saying that they were unimportant. He got Mr. Wickfield to allow him to draw out from the bank £1,200 belonging to a Trust Fund[1] saying that it was for certain things which had already been paid for. He made this seem as if Mr. Wickfield had done it, and has used it ever since as a way of forcing Mr. Wickfield to do whatever he wanted."

"You shall prove this, Copperfield!" said Uriah. Mr. Micawber continued:

"I lived in Heep's house after he left it. I found the remains of a pocket-book which he had burnt."

"Uriah! Uriah!" cried Mrs. Heep; "be humble. Make some arrangement with them."
"Mother! Will you be quiet!"

"I know that on many occasions Heep has changed the account books. He also made Mr. Wickfield sign a paper showing that money had been lent to Mr. Wickfield to save him from dishonour, although this money had never been lent. I have also a paper in which he practised writing Mr. Wickfield's name."

Heep took his keys and opened a certain cup-

---

[1] Trust fund = money trusted to Mr. Wickfield's charge.

board; then suddenly he thought of what he was doing and turned again towards us.

"Uriah," said the mother, "be humble and make an arrangement. When Mr. Traddles told me upstairs that he had found out everything, I promised him that you would be humble and pay back the money."

Mr. Micawber went on:

"I can show that Heep forced Mr. Wickfield to take him as a partner, promising to pay him a certain amount of money every year; that he pretended to lend money to Mr. Wickfield (this money being Mr. Wickfield's own money), and so got him into his power.

"I shall prove these things are true, and then I shall, with my unhappy family, disappear from the earth in which we serve no useful purpose."

Mr. Micawber finished his reading. He handed the paper to my aunt.

There was a large iron safe[1] in the room. Uriah went to it and opened it; it was empty.

"Where are the account books?" he cried. "Some thief has taken the books."

"I did," said Mr. Micawber.

"I have them," said Traddles.

My aunt suddenly ran at Uriah and seized him.

"Do you know what I want?" she said. "I want my money. Agnes, my dear, so long as I believed that Mr. Wickfield had taken my money I would not say a word! But now I know that this fellow did it, and I'll have it."

---

[1] Safe = iron box.

Uriah sat down.

"What do you want me to do?" he said.

"You will sign a paper," said Traddles, "giving everything to me. If you do not do this, you will go to prison."

Mrs. Heep broke out again, begging Agnes to help them and to have mercy.

"Mother! Hold your noise!" he said. "Well, let me have the paper. I'll sign it."

.   .   .   .

We were all very grateful to Mr. Micawber and eager to tell him so. We went home with him. His house was not far off. The street door opened into the sitting-room, and he ran in.

"Emma!" he cried, and rushed into Mrs. Micawber's arms.

"Emma," he said, "the cloud has passed from my mind. Now welcome hunger and rags; our trust in each other will support us to the end."

"Mr. Micawber," said my aunt, "I wonder that you have never thought of going out of England—to some other land, to Australia."

"I have long dreamt of doing so," said Mr. Micawber (though I believe he had never thought of it before). "But there is a difficulty."

"Money?" said my aunt. "But you are doing us a great service. We should like to give you the money."

"I could not receive it as a gift. But, if it could be lent to me——"

"Of course," said my aunt.

"Is the country of such a kind," asked Mrs.

Micawber, "that a man of Mr. Micawber's powers would have a fair chance of rising? I would not expect him to become Governor, but might he find reasonable openings for his powers?"

"There is no better chance anywhere," said my aunt.

We walked through the market-place, and Mr. Micawber had already taken upon himself the manner of an Australian farmer and looked at the sheep in a knowing way.

Forty

THE END OF HEEP

My aunt Agnes and I went back to Canterbury to meet Traddles and deal with the business of Wickfield & Heep. My aunt did not look well. Her face was white and there were deep lines on it and sometimes she wept and hid her tears with her hand.

"Mr. Wickfield is much better," said Traddles when we had all met together. "He has been able to help us a great deal in getting things clear. Having got everything into order I find that Mr. Wickfield owes nothing to anyone. There is a small amount—some hundreds of pounds—on which he may live."

"Next, Miss Trotwood," continued Traddles; "your money——"

"Well," said my aunt, "if it is gone, I can bear it. If it is not, I shall be glad to get it back."

"I can find only five——"

"Five thousand?" said my aunt, "or five pounds?"

"Five thousand," said Traddles.

"It was all there was," answered my aunt. "When I lost the money I thought that Mr. Wickfield had used it. Deceived by Heep, he wrote me a mad letter saying that he was a thief. I visited him early one morning; I burnt his letter and told him that, if he could set things right, he should do so, and, if he could not, he should keep silent."

"What happened to Heep?" said my aunt.

"I don't know. He left here."

"And now, about Mr. Micawber," said my aunt.

"Well, really," said Traddles, "I must give Mr. Micawber high praise. He might have been paid highly by Uriah Heep to keep silent.—He owes one hundred and three pounds five shillings."

"Agnes, my dear, what shall we give him? Five hundred pounds?"

"I think it would be better," said Traddles, "to pay for his journey to Australia and give him a small amount of money for his use."

Mr. and Mrs. Micawber were called into the room. My aunt told him what we had arranged.

"Now my advice to you," said I, "is never to allow anyone to lend you money again."

"Never," said Mr. Micawber. "I shall write such a vow upon the white page of my future life. I hope that my son Wilkins will ever remember that he had far better put his hand in the fire than let it touch those creatures, money-lenders, who have poisoned the life-blood of his unhappy parent."

Forty-one

THE STORM

It was evening when I set out in the coach along the road to Yarmouth.

"Don't you think," I said to the coachman, "that that is a very strange sky? I don't remember ever to have seen one like it."

"Nor I," said the coachman. "The sky shows that there will be wind, sir. There will be damage done at sea."

The sky was thickly covered with clouds, here and there touched with yellow, like smoke from wet wood. There were flying clouds, and clouds built up in mountains that seemed higher than their distance from the earth; and the moon drove through all as if she had lost her way and was very frightened.

There had been wind all day. It was rising with a strange and fearful sound. In another hour it was blowing harder.

As night came on the clouds closed in and covered the whole sky; it was very dark, and the wind blew harder. It increased until our horses could hardly face it; several times they turned about and stopped and we feared that the coach would be turned over.

When day came the wind blew harder and harder. I had been in many storms, but I had never known anything like this. We came to Ipswich, very late, having had to fight every inch of the ground. We found people standing in the market-place; they had got out of bed for fear of falling chimneys. While the horses were being changed they told us of roofs torn off, and of trees torn out of the earth.

Still the storm increased.

As we came struggling on, nearer and nearer to the sea from which this great wind was blowing, its force became greater and greater. Long before we came to the sea, its salt was on our lips and salt rain showered upon us.

When we came in sight of the sea the waves looked like another shore with towers and buildings on it.

I stayed at an old inn. I went out and found my way to the sea-shore. Half the people of the town were there. I found weeping women whose husbands were away in fishing-boats, old sailors shaking their heads as they looked at sea and sky, ship-owners excited and anxious.

Flying stones and sand blinded me: the noise of the sea beat upon my ears. High walls of water rolled in and seemed as if they would swallow the town. A boatman pointed. Then, oh, heaven, I saw it close in upon us—a wreck.

One *mast* was broken off and lay over the side and beat upon the ship as it rolled. The men were trying to cut the mast away; among them I saw one man with long curling hair. Then there was a great cry heard above the noise of wind and water. The sea came over the rolling wreck and carried away men, mast—everything into the boiling waters.

The second mast was still standing. The ship was breaking in the middle. There was a great cry of pity from those on the beach. Four men came up with the wreck, holding on to the remaining mast. Among them was the man with curling hair.

There was a bell on the ship. As the ship rolled or turned towards the shore or sprang wildly towards the sea, the bell rang: it sounded like a death-bell for those unhappy men. Now we could not see the ship; again she rose. Two men were gone. Men moaned, and women cried aloud and turned away their faces. Some ran wildly up and down the shore crying for help where no help could be. It was impossible to send a boat. No man would be so mad as to try to swim out with a rope. Then I saw the people moving, and Ham came to the front.

I saw on his face a grave determination. He looked out to sea,—and I understood his danger. I held him back with both arms and prayed the men around me not to let him leave the sand.

Another cry arose on shore. Looking to the wreck we saw the cruel sail with blow on blow beat off one of the men. One man was now left alone on the mast.

"Master Davy," said Ham, holding me by both hands, "if my time has come, it is come. May God bless you.—I'm going off."

I saw him standing there with a rope tied round him.

The wreck was breaking up, breaking in the middle. The one man still held on. He had a strange red cap. We saw him wave it, and that action brought an old memory to my mind—of a once dear friend.

Ham watched the sea. Then, as a great wave ran backwards, he ran in after it and in a moment was fighting with the water, rising with the hills, falling with the valleys. Then he was drawn again to land. They pulled him in quickly. He was hurt. I saw blood on his face, but he took no notice of that. He seemed to be ordering them to leave him more free. He went back.

Now he was swimming towards the wreck, rising with the hills, falling with the valleys, carried back towards the shore, carried on towards the ship, fighting hard.—At last he reached the wreck. In a moment he would be holding on to it. Then a high green hill of water came from beyond the ship. He seemed to leap into it;—and the ship was gone.

They drew him in almost to my feet—dead. He had been beaten to death by the great wave. He was carried to the nearest house. I remained near him. His gentle heart was for ever still.

As I sat beside the bed a fisherman came to me and whispered my name at the door.

"Sir," he said, "will you come here?"

A thought came to me. I leaned on his arm to support me.

"Has a body come on shore?"

He said, "Yes."

"Do I know it?" I asked.

He did not answer, but led me to the shore. On that part of it where Emily and I had looked for shells, among the ruins of the home which he had wronged, I saw him lying with his head upon his arm, as I had often seen him lie at school—Steerforth!

In that hour when we last spoke together (which I so little thought to be our last) he said, "Think of me at my best." I have done that, ever.

Forty two

MRS. STEERFORTH IS TOLD

On a golden autumn day, about noon, I arrived at Highgate. The little servant opened the door.

"I have some bad news for Mrs. Steerforth. Is she at home?"

She was in his room, not her own. At her side was Rosa Dartle. Mrs. Steerforth looked at me. The course of her thoughts seemed to stop and change.

"My son is ill?" she said. "You have seen him? You are friends again?"

With my lips I said to Rosa. "Dead."

She put her hand to her heart.

"Rosa, come to me!"

She came, but with no kindness or gentleness. Her eyes were like fire.

"Now," she said, "is your pride satisfied, mad woman?"

Mrs. Steerforth had fallen back in her chair looking at her with wide eyes.

"Oh," cried Miss Dartle, beating her breast, "see what your dead son did to me!" She pointed to the mark on her face.

"Oh, moan! proud mother of a proud and evil son. You made him what he was. I loved him better than you loved him and asked nothing in return. When he was freshest and truest he loved me. Then I became a plaything for an empty hour, to be dropped, or taken up as his fancy moved him. We fell away from each other. Since then I have been a mere thing, a broken, useless thing between you both."

"Miss Dartle," said I, "can you not feel for a mother in her grief?"

"Who feels for me?" she cried.

"No one can have loved him better than I. In such an hour forget his faults. Look at her and give her some help."

Unmoving, stiff, like a figure in stone, Mrs. Steerforth lay. Miss Dartle began to loose her dress.

"A curse upon you," she said. "It was in an evil hour that you came here. A curse upon you. Go!"

She had taken Mrs. Steerforth in her arms. She was kissing her, calling to her, trying by every means to call her back to sense and life.

Forty three

THE SHIP SAILS

My old nurse, Peggotty, and I went down to Gravesend to see the Micawbers start for Australia, and with them Mr. Peggotty.

The Micawber children were all crying. They hung upon Agnes to the last. Then they went off in a boat to the ship.—We found Mr. Peggotty waiting for us on the ship. He told us that at the last moment Mr. Micawber was seized for debt, but that he had paid the money and set him free. Not far away I saw, sitting with the Micawber children, a figure like Emily's; and I saw Agnes part from her with a kiss.

I saw Mrs. Gummidge helped by some younger women arranging Mr. Peggotty's goods.

All visitors were leaving the ship. The time was come. I said good-bye with Peggotty weeping on my arm. We got down into our boat and waited to see the ship start. It was a calm and beautiful sunset.

There was silence for a moment. Then the sails rose to the wind, and the ship began to move.

Forty four

THE LAST CHAPTER

I travelled in Italy and France and Switzerland. At last I returned home. I went to my aunt's house at Dover, and was received by her, Mr. Dick and dear Peggotty (who now acted as housekeeper), with tears of joy.

My aunt and I talked far into the night.

"And when, Trot, are you going over to Canterbury?" said my aunt.

"I shall ride over to-morrow morning," I answered.

I sat looking thoughtfully into the fire. I was thoughtful because I could not but feel sorry for what I had failed to learn in my younger life.

"Oh, Trot," I seemed to hear my aunt say, and I understood her better now, "Blind, blind, blind."

"You will find her father a white-haired old man," said my aunt, "you will find her as good, as beautiful, as unselfish as she has always been."

"Has Agnes any——"

"What? Any what?" said my aunt sharply.

"Any lover?" said I.

"Twenty!" cried my aunt. "She might have married twenty times."

"But is there any lover who is worthy of her? Does she love one?"

"I think there is one," said my aunt gravely. "She has never told me,—but I think so."

I rode away early in the morning. I asked the new servant who opened the door to tell Miss Wickfield that a gentleman wished to see her.

I heard a door open, and turned. Her beautiful calm eyes met mine as she came towards me. She stopped, and laid her hand upon her heart.

"Agnes, my dear girl, I have come too suddenly upon you."

"No, no. I am so glad to see you, Trotwood."

We sat down, side by side. She was so true, so beautiful, so good. I tried to bless her, to thank her, to tell her what she had done for me.

"And now, Agnes," I said, "tell me about yourself."

"What should I tell?" she said. "Father is well. You see us here, quiet in our own home.

"You are thoughtful, Trotwood."

"Agnes, shall I tell you what I am thinking about? I came to tell you. I learned that there is someone whom you love. Do not shut me out of what concerns your happiness so nearly. If you can trust me——"

She rose. She put her hands before her face, and broke into such tears as struck me to the heart.·

"Agnes, sister, dearest! What have I done?"

"Let me go away, Trotwood. I'm not well. I will speak to you—another time."

Agnes and David

I took her in my arms. "Agnes, ever my guide and best support."

Close in my arms she lay, nearer to my heart, her hand upon my shoulder, her sweet eyes shining through her tears on mine.

"I went away, Agnes, loving you. I stayed away, loving you. I returned home, loving you."

She laid her gentle hands upon my shoulders and looked calmly in my face.

"There is one thing which I must say."

"Dearest, what? Tell me."

"I have loved you all my life."

QUESTIONS

D.C. = David Copperfield.   P. = Peggotty.   Mr. M. =
Mr. Murdstone.   Mrs. G. = Mrs. Gummidge.   Mr. C. =
Mr. Creakle.   S. = Steerforth.   L.E. = Little Emily.
M. = Micawber.   Mr. D. = Mr. Dick.   U.H. = Uriah
Heep.   D.S. = Dr. Strong.   Mr. W. = Mr. Wakefield.

1. 1. Who died before D.C. was born?
   2. Who came to the door?
   3. What did Miss Betsy say of my mother?

   1. Who is Peggotty?
   2. Who is Mr. Chillip?
   3. Is the baby a boy or a girl?

2. 1. What seemed very big?
   2. What had D.C. been doing?
   3. What did D.C. ask? " If you marry a person and the
      person dies, you may——" (What?)

   1. Who was with my mother?
   2. Where did the gentleman put his hand?
   3. P. said, " It is pleasant to——" (What?)
   1. Who would not have liked Mr. M.?
   2. What did the gentleman do next Sunday?
   3. What did P. do which hurt me?

   1. Where will D.C. stay?
   2. Who is Ham?
   3. In what will D.C. go?
   4. Why was Mr. M. angry?

3. 1. What had P. on her knee?
   2. How tall was Ham?
   3. What was the house?

   1. What things were used as chairs?
   2. What was the bedroom?
   3. What smell was in the house?
   4. What did they have for dinner?

1. Was Ham P.'s son?
2. Whose daughter was L.E.?
3. Who was Mr. G.?
4. With whom did D.C. walk by the sea?

1. What had Mrs. G. been?
2. What does Mrs. G. do more than other people?
3. Of whom had Mrs. G. been thinking?

1. Why was D.C. sad?
2. What was at the door?
3. What has D.C. got?
4. Who sat on the other side of the fire?

4.
1. What did D.C. do till he fell asleep?
2. What must Clara (D.C.'s mother) be?
3. How does Mr. M. make a horse or a dog obey?

1. What was on Miss M.'s boxes?
2. Where did Miss M. keep her money?
3. Of what will Miss M. take care?
4. Where cannot D.C.'s mother live?
5. What did Miss M. do if D.C.'s mother said anything?

1. In what way were my lessons used?
2. What did D.C. do when Mr. M. looked up?
3. How did Mother try to help D.C.?
4. What did Mr. M. do to D.C.?
5. What was D.C.'s way of escaping?

5.
1. What has often happened to Mr. M.?
2. What did D.C. do to Mr. M.'s hand?
3. What did Mr. M. do to D.C.?
4. What did Miss M. put down?

6.
1. For how many days did D.C. stay there?
2. Where will D.C. go?
3. Why were my mother's eyes red?
4. What came to the gate?

7.
1. What did P. put into my pockets?
2. What was the money?
3. Who was Barkis?
4. What must D.C. tell P.?

1. Who ate most of the dinner?
2. What did they do at the school?
3. Why must George take care of the boy?

1. Who was Mr. Mell?
2. What people live in almshouses?
3. What was the name of the school?
4. Who was Mr. C.?
5. What did Mr. Mell do when he had finished writing?

8. 1. Who began to clear up the building?
   2. Who was the first boy who came back?
   3. Who was J. Steerforth?
   4. How much money had D.C.?
   5. What did they have that night?
   6. What will S. do?

9. 1. Whom did Mr. C. beat most of all?
   2. Who treated Mr. Mell badly?
   3. What had I told to S.?

1. What day was it?
2. Who was in charge?
3. What position does S. use?
4. What did S. call Mr. Mell?

1. Who came in?
2. What did Mr. C. tell Mr. Mell to do?
3. Who were the visitors?
4. Who came into the room?

10. 1. Had Mr. Barkis had an answer?
   2. " An answer to what? " What must D.C. say?
   3. Where did Barkis write the names?
   4. What had my mother in her arms?

1. What does Mr. Barkis want?
2. What does " slap " mean?
3. For what may Betsy forgive David?
4. What could David see on Mr. M.'s hand?

1. How long are the holidays?
2. Where did D.C. sit?
3. What does " sullen " mean?
4. What did Miss M. say when D.C.'s mother kissed him?

11. 1. What had Mrs. C. in her hand?
  2. What did the letter say?
  3. Who was in the carrier's cart?
  1. Who met D.C. at the gate?
  2. Where was Mr. M.?
  3. What was Miss M. doing?

12. 1. Where was D.C. allowed to go?
  2. What will P. do?
  3. What had L.E. to do?
  1. What did Barkis leave?
  2. What did P. do when she came back from the walks?
  3. What is P.'s name now?

13. 1. What came now?
  2. What were D.C.'s only friends?
  3. What will D.C. do?
  4. Where was the coach going?

14. 1. How many other boys were in the office?
  2. What was the name of the fat man?
  3. Where are D.C.'s lodgings?
  1. How many children had Mrs. M.?
  2. What difficulties has M.?
  3. Who were the only people who came to the house?
  4. What was Mrs. M. doing at six o'clock?
  5. What does " in case anything turns up " mean?
  1. Where was M. taken?
  2. Where did D.C. go on the last Sunday before?
  3. What brings the result: Happiness?
  4. What did M. do in order to make his idea clear?
  1. To whom will D.C. go?
  2. What did the young man seize?
  3. What did D.C. start to do?
  4. Where did D.C. sleep?
  5. How much did D.C. get for his coat?
  1. Where was my aunt?
  2. What did Mr. D. seem to be?
  3. " What shall I do with him? " What did Mr. D. say?
  4. What can't D.C.'s aunt understand?
  5. What should D.C.'s aunt do with D.C. now?

15. 1. What was Mr. D.'s brother going to do?
2. About what does Mr. D. talk?
3. What did Mr. D. show to D.C.?
1. Who arrived at the cottage?
2. What has Mr. M. come to do?
3. What would Mr. D. do with D.C.?
1. Why does Mr. M. hate D.C.?
2. What did Mr. M. tell D.C.'s mother?
3. What will D.C. be called?

16. 1. At what did Mr. D. work each day?
2. Why did he never get any distance in the letter?
3. How was D.C.'s name shortened?
1. Where will D.C. go to school?
2. Who opened the door? (Name.)
3. What colour were Uriah's eyes?
4. What were Uriah's hands like?
1. What was there above the fireplace?
2. What was the name of the gentleman?
3. Where will D.C. be left?
4. What was the name of Mr. W.'s daughter?
1. What must D.C. never be?
2. What did Agnes do after dinner?
3. What was Uriah's hand like?

17. 1. What was the name of the headmaster?
2. Who was Annie?
3. How many boys were in the schoolroom?
4. How did D.C. feel among the boys?
1. What did D.C. do as soon as school was finished?
2. Where was Agnes?
3. What did Mr. W. do after dinner?
4. What is there wherever Agnes goes?

18. 1. What was U.H. doing?
2. What does " humble " mean?
3. What is a sexton?
4. Who was a sexton?
1. What did U.H. do as he spoke?
2. Whom does D.C.'s aunt admire?
3. What will D.C. perhaps do in the end?
4. What did U.H.'s hand feel like?

19. 1. What was D.S. doing?
2. To whom did D.S. give his coat?
3. What did P. say about Mr. and Miss M.?
1. How often did D.C. go to Dover?
2. When did Mr. D. come over?
1. What did Mr. D. make?
2. How did Mr. D. stand when he spoke to D.S.?
3. What did D.S. do to Mr. D.?

20. 1. What had D.C. promised to do?
2. What did D.C. offer to teach U.H.
3. Was Mrs. Heep taller or shorter than U.H.?
1. About what had my aunt advised me to be silent?
2. What did D.C. find himself doing?
3. What man came down the street?
1. What was D.C. eager to do?
2. Where was M. staying?
3. What has Mrs. M. in this place?
4. What did M. tell D.C.?
1. Who were walking arm-in-arm?
2. What did M. say about U.H.?
3. Where will M. soon be?
4. What was M. eating?

21. 1. What did D.C. and his aunt often talk about?
2. To whom did D.C. say good-bye?
3. To whom will D.C. turn when in trouble?
1. What bad thing is Mr. W. doing?
2. What happens when Mr. W. is at his worst?
3. Who helped D.C. to pack his box?
1. Whom did D.C. see in the hotel?
2. Where will D.C. stay?
3. What was the name of the other lady?
1. By what was the mark made on Miss Dartle's cheek?
2. Where were S.'s letters kept?
3. Who was Littimer?

22. 1. To whose house did D.C. go first?
2. Where was Barkis?
3. What was under the bed?

1. What has Ham done?
2. To whom did S. talk?
3. What did S. say about L.E.?

23.
1. Who was sitting alone in P.'s house?
2. What does S. wish he could do?
3. What has S. bought?
4. Who has come?
5. What will be the name of the boat?
1. What did L.E. do when she saw S.?
2. Who was following Ham and L.E.?
3. What did Miss Mowcher do?
4. What could S. show Miss Mowcher?
1. Who was outside Barkis's house?
2. What was the name of the poor woman?
3. Where does she (question 2) want to go?
4. What did Ham give to her?

24.
1. What did S. agree to do?
2. What did D.C. become?
3. Whom did D.C. see in the theatre?
4. What must D.C. ask his friends to do?
1. How many letters did D.C. write?
2. Against whom does Agnes warn D.C.?
3. What will Uriah be?
1. To whom is Mr. W.'s whole mind given?
2. Who was at the party?
3. In what way did U.H. close his hand?
1. Whom does U.H. love?
2. What was U.H.'s plan?
3. Where did U.H. sleep?
4. What did Agnes seem to be doing in the dream?

25.
1. What is the name of Mr. Spenlow's daughter?
2. Who is the daughter's friend?
3. What came running along the path?
4. In what way was D.C. thinking of Mr. Spenlow?

26. Who came to supper? (A, B, C.)
2. Who came into the room?
3. When will S. be here?

    1. Who came up the stairs?
    2. From where has S. come?
    3. Who is very ill?
    4. How must D.C. think of S.?

27. 1. How as Barkis lying in bed?
    2. Where was the chair?
    3. What were the last words Barkis had said?
    4. When did Barkis die?

28. 1. What was Mr. P. doing?
    2. What was P. doing?
    3. What did Mr. P. put in the window?
    1. What did Ham tell D.C.?
    1. What question did Mr. P. ask?
    2. What is the name of the man?
    3. Where is Mr. P. going?
    4. What will Mr. P. break?

29. 1. Whom did Mr. P. see?
    2. Who was standing behind Mrs. S.?
    1. What last words does Mr. P. leave for L.E.?

30. 1. Who was Miss Mills?
    2. Who was Jip?
    3. Where will Dora stay?
    4. Dora and I were what?
    5. What does " engaged " mean?

31. 1. Who was in D.C.'s room?
    2. On what was my aunt sitting?
    3. What has happened to the aunt?

32. 1. What is the first thing which D.C. must do?
    2. Who would not agree to set D.C. free?
    3. What did Mr. Jorkins say? " If . . . I can't agree."
    1. Whom did D.C. see?
    2. Who is with Agnes?
    3. What will be stronger if wrong is being done?
    4. How much will the aunt get from her cottage?
    5. For whom may D.C. work?

1. What was in the window?
2. Who came in?
3. U.H. said that he would be happy if . . . (What?)

1. When did Mr. W. become like his own self?
2. What did the beggar say?
3. What did I see?
4. Where was D.S.?

1. What sort of book was D.S. writing?
2. Of what were D.S.'s pockets full?
3. From whom did D.C. receive a letter?
4. What has M. been asked to do?
5. What will U.H. do if M. . . . (Not pay very much but he will . . .)

33. 1. Did Dora know of the loss of D.C.'s aunt's money?
    3. What " foolish question " did D.C. ask Dora?
    3. What did D.C. tell Dora to look at?
    4. To what will Miss Mills draw Dora's mind?

34. 1. How was Mr. Spenlow looking?
    2. Whom did D.C. see in the room?
    3. What did Miss M. take out of her bag?
    4. With what was the dog playing?
    1. What does Mr. Spenlow tell D.C. to do with the letters?
    2. For how long must D.C. think over what Mr. Spenlow has said?
    3. Who was old Tiffey?
    4. How was Mr. Spenlow killed?

35. 1. Where was M.?
    2. What has Uriah done for M.?
    3. What did D.C. see in M.?
    1. In whom is D.C.'s trust?
    2. To whom will U.H. drink?
    3. At what did Mr. W. look?
    4. What did Uriah want to be?
    1. What has Mr. W. remembered too much?
    2. What did Mr. W. think to be possible?
    3. What was U.H.'s voice like?
    4. What can U.H. do?

36. 1. How was Dora treated by all?
    2. What did D.C.'s aunt call Dora?
    3. For what did Dora ask?
    4. What did the accounts do to Dora?
    5. What could Dora do if D.C. asked for an Irish stew?
    6. For what was the cookery book used?

37. 1. What was the name of the servant?
    2. At what time is dinner?
    3. What things were missing when Mary Ann left?
    4. What thing did one young woman wear?
    1. What did everyone seem to do?
    2. What did the people in the shops bring out?
    3. How much butter did they use?
    4. What name does Dora wish to be called?

38. 1. What servants did D.C. and Dora have?
    2. What did the boy steal?
    3. Why do the people become bad?
    4. What did Dora say? " If you are unhappy why . . . ? "
    1. What did D.C. decide to do?
    2. What would D.C. do now?
    3. What had D.C. hoped would come?
    4. What did Dora seem?
    5. What will Dora soon do?
    1. For how long was Dora ill?
    2. What did Jip seem to have become?

39. 1. What did D.C. receive?
    2. Where will he meet M.?
    3. About what subject does M. not wish to speak?
    1. What is the cause of the evil?
    2. Where will they meet?
    3. With whom did D.C. go to Canterbury?
    4. Where did they find M.?
    1. Where is Mr. W.?
    2. Who came in?
    3. Why does M. wait?
    4. What does " scoundrel " mean?
    1. Whom did Traddles lead in?
    2. By whom was the business of Wickfield & Heep done?
    3. How much was M. paid?
    4. In what way were M.'s services used?

1. By what was M.'s heart changed?
2. What is a trust fund?
3. Where did M. live?
4. What did M. find?
5. What had U.H. done on the paper?

1. What did Mrs. M. promise to Traddles?
2. What did U.H. pretend to do?
3. What is a safe?
4. What has M. taken?

1. What did the aunt believe?
2. What paper must U.H. sign?
3. Where will he go if he does not sign the paper?
4. What was Mrs. M.'s first name?
5. What manner had M. taken upon himself?

40. 1. How much does Mr. W. owe?
2. How much money had Miss Trotwood?
3. What did Mr. W. write in his letter to Miss Trotwood?

1. What happened to Heep?
2. How much money does M. owe?
3. What advice did D.C. give to M.?

41. 1. What was strange?
2. What does the sky show?
3. What did the horses do several times?

1. To what town did they come?
2. Why have the people got out of bed?
3. What did the waves look like?

1. Who were excited and anxious?
2. What did I see close in upon us?
3. What were the men trying to cut away?
4. What had one of the men?

1. Where was the ship breaking?
2. How many men came up with the wreck?
3. What was there on the ship?
4. Who came to the front?
5. What was tied round him? (Question 4.)

1. How many men were still holding on to the wreck?
2. What sort of cap had the man?
3. What did I see on Ham's face?
4. What came from beyond the ship?

1. How had Ham been killed?
2. What had come on to the shore?
3. Who was he?

42. 1. Who was at Mrs. S.'s side?
2. What were Miss Dartle's eyes like?

43. 1. Why did P. and D.C. go to Gravesend?
2. What had happened to M. at the last moment?
3. Who is going with Mr. P.?

44. 1. To whose house did I go?
2. Who was my aunt's housekeeper?
3. When will D.C. go to Canterbury?
4. Does Agnes love anyone?
1. What did Agnes do when D.C. said, " I learn that there is someone whom you love "?
2. What is the one thing which Agnes must say?